The Alex Techniqu

BEING BIG IN THE CITY

Charles Peattie was born in Manchester in 1958. He studied Fine Art at St Martins, but somehow, tragically, ended up drawing cartoons of men in suits for a living.

Russell Taylor was born in York in 1960. He read Russian at Oxford. He is still waiting for the call from MI6.

They began collaborating on Alex in the short-lived *London Daily News* in 1987. From there they moved, via a four-year stint at the *Independent*, to the *Daily Telegraph* where Alex appears five times a week.

They both live in London, but not yet in the postal districts to which they aspire. Charles has two children, Russell has a pampered cat.

Also by Charles Peattie and Russell Taylor
published by Headline

ALEX CALLS THE SHOTS
ALEX PLAYS THE GAME
ALEX KNOWS THE SCORE
ALEX SWEEPS THE BOARD
ALEX FEELS THE PINCH
THE FULL ALEX

The Alex Technique

BEING BIG IN THE CITY

Russell Taylor

With Alex cartoons by Charles Peattie and Russell Taylor

HEADLINE

First published in 1999
By HEADLINE BOOK PUBLISHING

10 9 8 7 6 5 4 3 2 1

ISBN 07472 7461 4

Typeset by Letterpart Limited, Reigate, Surrey
Designed by John Hawkins
Printed and bound in Italy by
Canale & C.S.p.A.
HEADLINE BOOK PUBLISHING
A division of the Hodder Headline Group
338 Euston Road
London NW1 3BH
www.headline.co.uk
www.hodderheadline.com

Contents

1 Tinker, Tailor, Investment Analyst, Risk Arbitrage Broker

Jobs in the City

You are sensible. Unlike your friends you have realised that you are never going to make it as a pop star. One day they will come to resent you deeply and probably try unsuccessfully to borrow money off you, but for the moment they think you are sad.

Perhaps you nosed around a careers fair in your freshman term. Maybe you were taken to see *Wall Street* for an eleventh birthday treat, but something (could it be natural greed

Alex
PEATTIE + TAYLOR.

IT'S FUNNY TO THINK THAT AT TWENTY-FIVE I EARN MORE THAN MY DAD...

YOU KNOW, MY MOTHER STILL REMEMBERS THE DAY WHEN HE FOUND OUT THAT I EARNED MORE THAN HIM...

HOW DID HE REACT?

APPARENTLY HE TORE UP MY TELEGRAM...

Alex
PEATTIE + TAYLOR.

SO WHAT EXACTLY IS YOUR JOB, ALEX?

WELL, PENNY, AS A CORPORATE FINANCIER I AM THE PRINCIPAL CHANNEL OF LIAISON WITH THE CLIENT...

BASICALLY THAT MEANS THAT I CHAIR THE MEETINGS. I HAVE TO ENSURE THAT WE GET THROUGH ALL THE ITEMS ON THE AGENDA.

IT'S THE MOST SENSIBLE ARRANGEMENT. YOU SEE EACH OF THE OTHER PEOPLE PRESENT - LAWYERS, ACCOUNTANTS AND SO ON WILL BE A SPECIALIST IN SOME INDIVIDUAL AREA OF EXPERTISE ESSENTIAL TO A TAKEOVER.

WHEREAS YOU'RE TOTALLY IGNORANT ABOUT EVERYTHING?

QUITE. SO IT'S IMPORTANT TO HAVE THE POWER TO CHANGE THE SUBJECT WHEN FACED WITH A TRICKY QUESTION.

and materialism?) draws you to the Square Mile. You know nothing about the City apart from the fact that it involves wearing red braces and talking on several phones at once . . . but you yearn for it. The respectability, the power, the frequent-flier points. But what particular area should you aim for? Where will you earn the most? Where will you get maximum responsibility? And, more important, where do you get the most freebies?

To aid you in your choice, here is a brief outline of some City jobs.

CORPORATE FINANCE

These are the people who try to generate fees for a merchant bank by convincing companies, who'd be much better off left on their own, to do deals. 'Corporate finance' is what graduates always answer when asked which area of the City they would like to specialise in, in the same way that people always say 'carrot' if asked to name a vegetable. This is strange as, for a trainee, corporate finance is actually the most murderous department to be assigned to. Everything you own, including your soul and your weekends, belongs to your bank. Your fourteen-hour days are spent photocopying, your

Alex PEATTIE + TAYLOR

NO OFFENCE, CLIVE, LAD, BUT I CAN'T SEE WHY I NEED A MERCHANT BANK FOR THIS DEAL. THE LAWYERS AND ACCOUNTANTS SEEM TO DO ALL THE WORK...

AH, BUT REMEMBER, MR HARDCASTLE, YOU'RE BRINGING YOUR COMPANY TO THE MARKET. THERE ARE COMPLEX CITY FACTORS THAT YOU AS A NORTHERN BUSINESSMAN COULDN'T POSSIBLY BE AWARE OF...

IF YOU WANT THE OFFER TO BE TAKEN UP, THE TIMING OF THE FLOTATION IS OF THE ESSENCE, WHICH IS WHERE YOU NEED THE SKILL AND JUDGEMENT OF AN EXPERIENCED CORPORATE FINANCIER LIKE ALEX HERE.

2ND WEEK IN JUNE'S NO GOOD... EVERYONE WILL BE AT ASCOT... MYSELF INCLUDED... AFTER THAT THERE'S THE LORDS TEST, THEN WIMBLEDON... HMM, BEST SCRUB THAT MONTH ALTOGETHER...

FLIP FLIP

DIARY

Alex PEATTIE + TAYLOR

THIS IS OBSCENE. YOU KNOW THAT ABORTIVE TAKEOVER BATTLE THAT'S JUST FINISHED IN THE CITY? THE TWO COMPANIES INVOLVED PAID OUT A TOTAL OF ALMOST £50 MILLION IN FEES TO ACHIEVE PRECISELY NOTHING...

GREEDY CORPORATE ADVISERS LIKE YOURSELF, ALEX, POCKETING ALL THAT MONEY WHICH COULD HAVE BEEN INVESTED IN THE COMPANIES' BUSINESSES OR RETURNED TO THE SHAREHOLDERS...

OH... I SAY, PENNY...

I'M SORRY, ALEX, BUT ISN'T IT A MATTER OF THE SLIGHTEST CONCERN TO YOU WHEN YOUR BANK HAS GRATUITOUSLY BLED A CORPORATION DRY?

WELL, IF YOU PUT IT THAT WAY...

I SUPPOSE IT MIGHT LEAVE THEM VULNERABLE TO A TAKEOVER BID. I'D BEST CHECK WHETHER THEY WANT TO RETAIN OUR SERVICES TO DRAW UP A DEFENCE STRATEGY...

JOT JOT

nights at the printers – an ordeal from which a 'due diligence' visit to a ball-bearing factory will seem like a merciful release.

The corporate financier is at the cutting edge of the City, in that you are obliged to deal directly with industrialists, some of whom have been known to dress in man-made fibres often in unseemly shades of light blue. This linking role between the City and people in real jobs who actually make things and get paid a quarter of what you do calls for many qualities: articulateness, diplomacy and, frankly, a great deal of patronising pomposity.

The attractive element is that you don't actually have to know very much to work in corporate finance. The job mainly involves bossing around all the people who have proper skills (lawyers, accountants) and then rubbing it in by getting paid more than them. This is the department where Alex nominally works so it's got to be quite a cushy number in the end.

ANALYST

Analysts (aka economists) research companies and produce reports on them which they hope will generate commission by persuading their clients, the fund managers, to deal.

Alex PEATTIE + TAYLOR

THESE DAYS WE'RE BEING ENCOURAGED TO TAKE INTO ACCOUNT A COMPANY'S RECORD ON SUCH FACTORS AS THE ENVIRONMENT, COMMUNITY AND EMPLOYEE RELATIONS RATHER THAN JUST PROFITS...

AH YES, CLIVE...

THE "SOCIAL AUDIT." NOTHING NEW IN THAT. AFTER ALL, CITY ECONOMISTS AREN'T JUST A BUNCH OF HARD-NOSED CAPITALISTS INTERESTED ONLY IN A COMPANY'S BALANCE SHEET.

NATURALLY THE FACT THAT AN ORGANISATION HAS INVESTED IN SOCIAL AND RECREATIONAL AMENITIES ON BEHALF OF ITS STAFF OR THE COMMUNITY COULD WELL AFFECT ANALYSTS' JUDGEMENT OF IT...

OFFER THEM A WEEKEND'S "FACT FINDING" VISIT THERE AND THEY'LL SAY ANYTHING YOU WANT ABOUT THE BUSINESS.

Alex PEATTIE + TAYLOR

BY THE WAY, HOW WAS THE EXTEL LUNCH?

AN EXCELLENT OCCASION, CLIVE, ATTENDED BY ALL THE USUAL SUSPENSE AND EXCITEMENT OF FINDING OUT WHO'S BEEN VOTED TOP ANALYST OF THE YEAR...

LONG LUNCH WAS IT?

NOT REALLY. YOU KNOW WHAT IT'S LIKE. PRETTY MUCH AS SOON AS THE RESULTS ARE ANNOUNCED EVERYONE GRABS THEIR COPY OF THE SURVEY AND TAKES OFF...

"OUTSIDE ONE IS GREETED WITH THE CUSTOMARY SPECTACLE OF ANALYSTS WHO HAVE DONE WELL IN THEIR SECTOR CROUCHED ON PORTABLE TELEPHONES, SURVEY OPEN ON THEIR LAPS, EXCITEDLY RELAYING THE NEWS...

THEY CAN'T WAIT TO GET BACK TO THE OFFICE, EH?

CLIVE... ONE DOESN'T PHONE ONE'S HEADHUNTER FROM THE OFFICE...

OH... RIGHT...

11

These reports are called 'notes', though as a 'note' may be 200 pages long, one dreads to think what would happen if the analyst ever got prolix.

An analyst will normally cover a particular sector (Petrochemicals, Biotech, etc.), the most desirable of which is undoubtedly Leisure, where you get to check out lots of bars and golf courses *and* get paid for doing so.

Much of an analyst's job involves compiling information on your sector, which can involve some punishing week-long research trips to companies in pleasant subtropical locations with nearby sporting amenities. The analyst's actual production of notes is concentrated into certain times of year: immediately before the votes are cast in the three major annual surveys of analysts, for example. But, of course, your most incisive work will be reserved for the month before the departmental bonuses are being worked out.

It is not the best job for the trainee as you will find yourself compiling all the research only to see your boss put his name on the note and take all the credit for it. The upside is that you may get to appear on TV (but only the early-morning financial programmes that your mum doesn't watch).

Alex
PEATTIE + TAYLOR

WHAT'S THAT YOU'RE PUTTING IN THE BIN, CLIVE?

IT'S ONLY SOME TEDIOUS POST-BUDGET ANALYSIS FAXED TO US BY AN ECONOMIST...

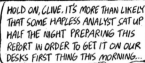

HOLD ON, CLIVE, IT'S MORE THAN LIKELY THAT SOME HAPLESS ANALYST SAT UP HALF THE NIGHT PREPARING THIS REPORT IN ORDER TO GET IT ON OUR DESKS FIRST THING THIS MORNING...

YES... SO?

WELL, UNDER THE CIRCUMSTANCES I THINK THE LEAST WE CAN DO IS CAST AN EYE OVER IT... AFTER ALL, IT'S BOUND TO CONTAIN SOME INFORMATION THAT MIGHT BE OF USE TO US... SUCH AS HERE, LOOK...

"TIME OF TRANSMISSION 3.37 AM"... HE MUST BE TOTALLY SHATTERED THIS MORNING. LET'S PHONE HIM UP AND ANNOY HIM BY ASKING ENDLESS NIT-PICKING QUESTIONS ABOUT LONG-TERM INTEREST RATE POLICIES...

REACH

CRUMPLE
TOSS

GOOD IDEA.

Alex
PEATTIE + TAYLOR

WELL THAT WAS A PRETTY HUGE ORDER YOU GAVE THAT STOCKBROKER AFTER A VERY SHORT CONVERSATION.

500,000 B.T. SHARES? YEAH.

YOU KNOW HOW IT IS... WHAT WE FUND MANAGERS NEED BROKERS FOR... HE'S AWARE OF WHAT OTHER PEOPLE ARE DOING IN THE MARKET AND HE HAPPENED TO HAVE PERTINENT PERSONAL INFORMATION HE WANTED TO SHARE WITH ME.

TAP
TAP

THESE GUYS ARE CLUED-UP, SEE? THEY CAN OFTEN BE A SOURCE OF CANDID ADVICE SUGGESTING THAT BUYING OR SELLING SOME STOCK WOULD ACCRUE TO ONE'S ADVANTAGE.

SO WHAT DID HE TELL YOU?

THAT ON THE AMMOUNT OF COMMISSION I'D GIVEN HIM SO FAR THIS YEAR HE WOULD ONLY BE ABLE TO INVITE ME TO THE LADIES' QUATER FINALS AT WIMBLEDON.

I HOPE YOU'RE NOW LOOKING AT THE MEN'S SEMIS AT LEAST...

13

FUND MANAGER

Fund managers are paid to invest money on behalf of their clients, who are normally large pensions funds.

Of all jobs in the City, apart from making cappuccino, theirs is the one that has most effortlessly been supplanted by machines. Nowadays fund managers have to compete with unmanaged 'Tracker' funds. These are weighted so that their composition conforms exactly to that of the FTSE 100. Thus, by definition they always perform as well as the index. By contrast, the vast majority of human fund managers consistently underperform the index yet charge their clients much more for this service. Whether you should want to work in an industry on which the whistle seems long overdue to be blown is debatable.

Fund managers usually claim not to place much value on the huge amount of research they receive from analysts, except when their fund underperforms (i.e. most years) when they can always pick out some bad stock recommendation and claim they followed it.

Fund management calls for a mathematical brain with an ability to assimilate and process information. For example, there will be constant pressure on you to dream up a new way of measuring your investment performance by which your fund is in the top

quartile when you make your regular reports to your clients (e.g.: 'No. 3 in Far East Long-Term High-Yield funds managed by a Pisces'). You will also have to gauge accurately how much commission to pay out to brokers so that you get invited to the men's semis at Wimbledon and not the drossy first week.

STOCKBROKER

Brokers are the interface between the analyst and the fund manager. Their job is to interpret the analyst's research and bring in orders from the client. Their role as intermediary is greatly at risk from computerised direct dealing, though the new generation of IT hardware is still not sophisticated enough at telling clients bad-taste jokes or entertaining them at lapdancing bars to pose an immediate threat.

Traditionally, the relationship between stockbrokers and fund managers has always been fairly shady. After a good day out at Wimbledon and a decent dinner afterwards at the broker's expense, the fund manager would be sure to place a big thank-you order the next day. Steps were rightly taken to iron out this blatantly self-interested entertaining of

Alex PEATTIE + TAYLOR

MANY TRADITIONAL STOCKBROKERS LIKE US ARE GETTING WORRIED ABOUT HOW THE RISE OF THE INTERNET WILL DAMAGE THEIR BUSINESS...

WITH THE SERVICE-PROVIDERS PUTTING MORE AND MORE REAL-TIME FINANCIAL DATA AND SHARE EXECUTION SYSTEMS ON-LINE OUR CLIENTS COULD SEE IT AS A VIABLE ALTERNATIVE TO USING A BROKING FIRM...

IT'S AT TIMES LIKE THIS THAT ONE STARTS TO HEAR ONE'S CLIENTS ASKING QUESTIONS ABOUT SERVERS AND SHOWING AN INTEREST IN WHAT'S GOING BACK AND FORTH ACROSS THE NET...

THAT'S TRUE.

WHO'S THAT SERVING?

SAMPRAS, I THINK. JOLLY GOOD RALLY WASN'T IT?

WHEN SOMEONE INVENTS A COMPUTER THAT CAN TAKE THEM TO WIMBLEDON THEN I'LL START WORRYING...

THWACK

email: alex-cartoon@etgate.co.uk

Alex PEATTIE + TAYLOR

SO THE BANK OF ENGLAND COMMISSIONED A REPORT INTO THE BARINGS FIASCO?

OH YES. THERE ARE ALWAYS ENQUIRIES AFTER EVENTS LIKE THIS, ESPECIALLY WHERE CONTROVERSIAL PRODUCTS LIKE DERIVATIVES ARE INVOLVED.

SO WHAT EXACTLY ARE THOSE THINGS, ALEX?

THEY'RE COMPLEX INSTRUMENTS EVOLVED BY THE FINANCIAL WORLD, PENNY. BASICALLY THEIR USE IS TO SHORE UP A POSITION WHICH MIGHT BE VULNERABLE TO A RUINOUS DOWNSIDE.

THESE MECHANISMS ALLOW THE INDIVIDUAL TO OFF-SET HIS LIABILITY THEREBY SHIELDING HIMSELF FROM THE DAMAGING CONSEQUENCES OF THINGS GOING WRONG... THIS I MUST STRESS IS THEIR ONLY DESIGNATED FUNCTION...

SO THAT'S WHAT A DERIVATIVE DOES?

ER, NO... THAT'S WHAT A BANK OF ENGLAND ENQUIRY DOES.

NO-ONE IN THE CITY HAS THE REMOTEST IDEA WHAT A DERIVATIVE DOES...

17

fund managers. Many fund management firms now have centralised dealing desks that will determine who commission is paid to, so stockbrokers now cut out the middleman and entertain the head of centralised dealing directly.

Much of a broker's skill base is interpersonal. You will typically have an effortless rapport with all the real movers and shakers in the City – i.e. maîtres d', golf club secretaries, PAs of FTSE 100 chairmen, etc. – so as to be able to facilitate a bored client who suddenly finds himself with a spare lunchtime at short notice.

TRADER

All sorts of things are traded in the City – bonds, financial futures, derivatives, debt – but essentially they are all just numbers on a screen, and the idea is to buy them cheap and sell them to your mate expensive, which is why this kneejerk function was traditionally filled by East End barrow boys.

Sadly, the advent of computerised trading has meant that the arbitrage opportunities (differences in prices) are becoming increasingly smaller. The consequence is that banks

have to deal in much larger amounts in order to make a decent profit. This is why human operatives (e.g. Nick Leeson) foul up so spectacularly when the market goes against them, to the immense satisfaction of newspaper editors and everyone else who isn't an employee or customer of the bank.

As a consequence of this, today's trader is more likely to be a rocket scientist (aka Quant) with a double First in Applied Mathematics than an ex-market stallholder from Essex. The Quant will spend weeks devising a computer program to exploit some tiny differential between the price of rupees in Hong Kong and Swedish mortgage rates. The potential downside to the bank with this arrangement is much smaller as it is fairly certain that the program the Quant has written will be impossible to explain to any of the bank's clients or salesmen and therefore will never be used.

FINANCIAL JOURNALIST

Financial journalists occupy a strange position in the City. Everyone is highly deferential to them due to the power that their written word in a national newspaper can wield, but,

ironically, all these fawning acolytes are actually paid immensely more than the object of their devotion.

Financial journalists don't actually know anything about the City. If they did they'd be earning five times their salary working as an analyst. So much of their work involves phoning brokers and PR people and asking them to explain it all.

The journalists' 'real world' salaries are partially compensated for by the huge number of invitations to corporate hospitality events they receive. Though not as bibulous as when all journalists were corralled together in Fleet Street, quite an impressive alcohol intake is still required for the serious investigative reporter. The main compensation is the hangover-friendly hours the journalist works, getting into work at about 10.30, especially if you've been out schmoozing a broker whom you know had to be at his desk by 7.15.

A financial journalist is the only person who will treat a graduate trainee in a bank with decency – not out of any *esprit de corps* arising from your very similar salary levels but because he knows that you are in possession of lots of price-sensitive information and might just be naïve enough to be bluffed into faxing it over.

FINANCIAL PR

Financial PR is a relatively new industry to the City, coming about largely as a result of the privatisations and contested bids of the 1980s. It exists as a buffer zone between industrial clients and the well-known terror they have of the City (especially financial journalists).

Financial PRs spend much of their time in behind-the-scenes negotiations with journalists, trying to get them to run puffs on their clients or, more important, trading off favours to keep damaging stories out of the newspapers.

The financial PR person is like the guy in the red jumper who got beamed down to the planet's surface with Captain Kirk et al. in *Star Trek*. You always knew that when things turned nasty he would be the one to get vaporised by the alien life force. Likewise, if a deal goes pear-shaped the PR firm will always be singled out for the blame. But, of course, when things go miraculously right the PR person will be muscled out of the queue to take the credit.

For all the downside of the fall guy status, financial PR does have its compensations, not least in the gratifyingly large number of lunches, golf days and assorted junkets that you will have to host.

Alex PEATTIE + TAYLOR

BUT MEGABANK IS PAYING US A LOT OF MONEY FOR THIS TIME AND MOTION STUDY OF THEIR CORPORATE FINANCE DEPARTMENT.

I KNOW...

BUT I FEEL DREADFUL ABOUT PRESENTING OUR RECOMMENDATIONS. AFTER ALL, I'M NOT JUST A MANAGEMENT CONSULTANT... I'M A HUMAN BEING AS WELL.

HOW CAN ONE CARE ABOUT THE STRICT APPLICATION OF ABSTRACT PRINCIPLES OF BUSINESS MANAGEMENT WHEN PEOPLE'S JOBS ARE AT STAKE HERE?

I MEAN SURELY WE CAN DO SOMETHING TO MAKE OUR FINDINGS A LITTLE LESS EXTREME?

HMMM...

YOU MEAN CLAIM THE DEPARTMENT IS RATHER INEFFICIENT AND RECOMMEND SOME CUTBACKS?

WELL, THEY WON'T BOTHER TO EMPLOY US AGAIN IF WE SAY EVERYTHING'S FINE.

Alex PEATTIE + TAYLOR

YOU'RE THINKING OF HAVING THE BANK PAY 500 GRAND FOR A MANAGEMENT CONSULTANT THIS YEAR?

IT WILL BE MONEY WELL SPENT IF WE CAN AVOID ANOTHER FIASCO LIKE THIS, ALEX...

IN MY OPINION IT WOULD BE A GOOD IDEA TO HAVE SOMEONE FROM OUTSIDE THE CORPORATE STRUCTURE TO ADVISE ON ANY CHANGES THAT MIGHT OR MIGHT NOT BE IMPLEMENTED.

THE TROUBLE IS: WHEN POLICY IS DECIDED _INTERNALLY_ ONE COMES UP AGAINST COMPANY POLITICS... ALL THE RECIPROCAL SIDE-TAKING AND OWED OBLIGATIONS WHERE A MESH OF PETTY LOYALTIES AND RIVALRIES MAKE IT IMPOSSIBLE TO COME TO A PROPER DECISION.

LIKE WHO'S GOING TO GET THE BLAME WHEN SOMETHING'S GONE WRONG..?

QUITE. WE STILL CAN'T DECIDE WHO'S TO CARRY THE CAN FOR THIS LOT. :YAWN:

NEXT YEAR WE COULD JUST SACK THE CONSULTANT.

MANAGEMENT CONSULTANT

These are people who don't know how to do any of the above jobs, and thus are called in by companies and paid huge consultancy fees. Their ignorance is not particularly an impediment to this role, which is normally just as the hatchetman who implements highly unpopular decisions on behalf of management. Thus, the consultants will bear all the opprobrium for a cost-cutting programme involving 500 redundancies. Of course, should the decision prove to be wrong, the consultants merely don their other hat, that of the scapegoat, and are given the sack. As long as there are spineless managers with bottoms that need covering there will always be work for management consultants. In short, excellent long-term career prospects here.

OTHER JOBS (SOLICITOR, ACCOUNTANT, ETC.)

All other jobs in the City are staffed by desperate wannabes. There are some superficial differences (accountants are dull, solicitors are pedantic), but basically they're just trying to get a foot in the back door to the lucrative world of corporate finance.

2 'Goal-Orientated Team Player'

Doctoring Your cv

Though the spectre of disintermediation, with machines replacing people, stalks the City, graduates are still vital to the financial world. While there are still human beings working there they will always need someone to fetch their coffee.

Graduate recruitment and training are thus very important parts of a bank's function. For a start they give the Human Resources department half its reason to exist. Senior directors from rival banks meeting up at gentlemen's clubs will boast to each other about their huge intake of graduates in the same way that rugby players do about pints of bitter.

29

Of course, in today's highly competitive financial world, organisations have to be much more progressive and proactive to secure the best candidates. To this end they will occasionally look beyond Oxford and Cambridge universities (though frankly not much further than Bristol or Durham).

Modern recruitment policies at Oxbridge are similar to those practised by the KGB during the Cold War. You will be targeted, vetted and approached by your future masters, especially if you are a precocious mathematics student. So the sad truth is that, if by your final year someone in a pinstripe suit hasn't shuffled up to you on a park bench muttering something about the snowdrops being out early this year, then you probably haven't been fast-tracked.

Never mind: there's still the conventional route. This starts much earlier than it used to. To Alex's generation, long vacations meant bumming your way round Greece or lazing in an armchair at your parents' house watching the Test match. Not so the new breed of students, who see three sun-drenched months stretching languorously ahead of them as the perfect opportunity to enhance their cv by doing a summer internship.

Summer, of course, is the very worst time for a graduate to get any experience of how the City works, as at that time of year basically it doesn't. If individual A isn't on holiday,

Alex PEATTIE+TAYLOR

WHAT'S THE POINT, CLIVE?... WE SPEND YEARS PREPARING OUR BRIGHTEST PUPILS TO BECOME HI-TECH SCIENTISTS AND ENGINEERS AND THEN THEY GET SNAPPED UP BY SOME FINANCIAL INSTITUTION...

I KNOW, HEAD-MASTER.

THESE DAYS I'M CONSTANTLY HEARING MY PUPILS TALKING ABOUT THE HUGE BONUSES THEY'VE BEEN OFFERED

TSK TSK.

AND DO YOU KNOW WHAT THEY SAY WHEN I SUGGEST THAT THEY SHOULD DECLINE THESE "BONUSES"?

NO.

"BONUS, BONORUM, BONUNT, SIR?"

OH DEAR.

COULDN'T HAPPEN IF WE'D STUCK TO GIVING THEM A PROPER CLASSICAL EDUCATION...

I SUPPOSE NOT...

Alex PEATTIE+TAYLOR

WHAT OUR BANK WILL BE LOOKING FOR IN GRADUATE RECRUITMENT WEEK IS HARD EVIDENCE OF YOUR ACHIEVEMENT, AMBITION AND GENERAL SUITABILITY TO A CAREER IN THE CITY...

THIS APPLIES FROM THE FIRST INFORMAL INTERVIEW WHEN WE LOOK OVER A CANDIDATE'S CURRICULUM VITAE, TO THE FINAL IN-DEPTH EXAMINATION ON THE BASIS OF WHICH A JOB OFFER MAY BE MADE.

BUT AT THIS INITIAL STAGE WE ARE NOT OVERLY DEMANDING. WHEN STUDENTS CAME UP FOR INTERVIEW LAST YEAR I BELIEVE ONLY 2 CVS WERE REJECTED OUT OF HAND...

...THOUGH IT'S UNLIKELY THAT ANYONE WHO HAD ARRIVED IN A SKODA OR A LADA WOULD HAVE GOT MUCH PAST THE DOOR EITHER.

then his client is, so either way there's no possibility of doing any work. Then when they're both back at the same time, A's boss will be on holiday, so there's no incentive to do any work, etc., etc. To cut a long story short, no one wants to be shadowed by a mustard-keen student asking you about bond-pricing models when you're trying to watch the cricket or sleep off a long lunch.

The second stage of the recruitment process is the Milk Round, where City firms come to universities (well, the posh ones anyway) to do presentations, with drinks and canapés afterwards. In Alex's day these were always well attended because it saved impoverished students having to eat in hall for a month. Today's bright-eyed careerist undergraduates are far more likely to possess a presentable suit and a detailed knowledge of the company's global positioning and less likely to be caught stuffing vol-au-vents into a duffel bag.

The bank will normally bring along a recent graduate from your university who can better bond with the students. Be aware, though, that the relationship works both ways, and this individual's recent familiarity with your alma mater will prevent you from being able to tell any outrageous fibs about being captain of the college football team or debating society.

Your next task will be to doctor your cv suitably. A few pointers on this:

Languages These are always good. Be warned, though, that their usefulness is seasonal. A year or two back, a Russian-speaking graduate was a prize find, as every company wanted to get a foot in the door of the ex-Soviet Union's emerging market, but no one senior wanted to have to travel to the godforsaken place. However, after the spectacular self-destruction of the Russian markets in 1998 the language of Pushkin has returned to its former obscurity without even the traditional decent career openings in counter-espionage.

European languages are vital in a modern global bank, but be wary of bumping up your GCSE and a summer exchange visit to 'fluent French' on your cv. Your interview panel may well include someone French who will put your rash claim to the test by conducting the entire interview in his native tongue.

Sport is very good, because it is associated with being a 'team player' (a belief which curiously pertains even if your game is squash or marathon running). Remember that in the modern global City, where most banks are owned by Americans, Swiss or Germans, an obscure minority sport like cricket (which only the English play and are useless at) is

Alex PEATTIE + TAYLOR

WHAT ARE YOU SWOTTING UP YOUR FRENCH FOR, CLIVE?

AN IMPORTANT PRESENTATION TOMORROW, BRIDGET.

ALEX SAYS THAT WHILE THESE FOREIGN CLIENTS' ENGLISH IS USUALLY FAIRLY FLUENT IT'S VITAL WE HAVE THE ABILITY TO COMMUNICATE WITH EACH OTHER CLEARLY...

BECAUSE THERE ARE ALWAYS A NUMBER OF UNFORSEEN COMPLICATIONS WHICH MIGHT CROP UP IN THE DISCUSSION OF BUSINESS VENTURES.

PAS DEVANT LES CLIENTS, CLIVE.

AH OUI. DISEZ NON PLUS, MON BRAVE.

Alex PEATTIE + TAYLOR

THESE DAYS ALL GRADUATES' C.V.s HAVE THE OBLIGATORY STRAIGHT 'A's AT SCHOOL, ONE -SOMETIMES TWO - UNIVERSITY DEGREES...

BUT ACADEMIA IS NOT THE BE-ALL-AND-END-ALL. WE WOULD NOT WANT TO EMPLOY SOME SAD WORKAHOLIC WHO WOULD HAVE NO LIFE AWAY FROM THE OFFICE...

NATURALLY NOT...

WHICH IS WHY ONE LOOKS FOR EVIDENCE IN A RESUMÉ OF A WELL-ROUNDED INDIVIDUAL...ONE WHO HAS PLENTY OF OUTSIDE HOBBIES AND INTERESTS...

YES.

WHICH WE CAN SCREW UP FOR HIM BY GIVING HIM AN URGENT REPORT TO WRITE AT 6·30 PM...

SO WHAT ARE YOU MISSING TONIGHT, PETERS? 5-A-SIDE FOOTBALL OR CHESS CLUB?

not as desirable as a more international sport like tennis or soccer (which everyone plays and the English are useless at).

Certainly, if you have represented your university at a sport be sure to mention it. Employers will be wary of hiring a graduate with a Master's Degree in Business because they know you will just show up their own ignorance on the subject. But if you have a football Blue you will be a potentially valuable resource in the bank's own five-a-side team, currently languishing in the second division of the Interbank League, and will be snapped up.

Work experience You will, of course, have several years' worth of internships and voluntary charity work to insert here. In Alex's day the best a candidate could honestly put under this section was a spell of working as a waiter. Ironically, it is this that would best qualify you for a job in the City, as being able to remember a complex sandwich order is what marks out the successful graduate trainee from the pack.

Hobbies and interests Unless they happen to coincide with the interviewer's own interests, these are not of much value. At best they will provide the material for polite conversation once the interviewer has decided you haven't got the job.

Don't put 'reading' – the only people who can expect to get any credit for being able

to read are aged under six. 'Travel' is also risky, as no matter how obscure the places you have visited, your interviewer will have gone there last year on a dismal tour of Third World dumps trying to drum up Emerging Market business and will have no desire to be reminded of a week of horror at the hands of room service in the Tashkent Hyatt.

Photo This is a tricky one. It depends on (a) how photogenic you are and (b) the sex of the person interviewing you. If you are quite presentable and of the opposite sex it might help, but remember that no boss wants to spend an indeterminate number of years sitting next to someone who is not only younger but also better-looking than himself. The recent breakthrough of woman through the 'glass ceiling' to genuine positions of managerial responsibility in banks has thankfully ensured that attractive female job applicants can no longer secure themselves an automatic interview by attaching a glamour shot of themselves to their résumé.

Driving licence Of course, preceded by the words 'clean, current' (strange how no one ever mentions it if they've got an out-of-date one with three endorsements), this is a formality on any cv but being able to drive could be a useful skill. If your boss finds he has failed to clock up the necessary number of company car miles by the end of the tax

Alex PEATTIE + TAYLOR

That's rather a generous donation to your old college.

Well, when I got the letter from the university to all its graduates asking for contributions...

I looked at the example of my grandfather, who as a successful businessman has never failed to lend his financial support to educational charities...

Because he's always regretted that lack of money prevented him from having the opportunity of a decent education himself... so making this donation gives me a good feeling...

Knowing that this is one appeal he could never be invited to contribute to.

Alex PEATTIE + TAYLOR

As a father, Alex, you must be worried by the upheavals taking place in the British education system.

Not really, Clive. On the whole I rather approve of the changes being proposed.

But, whatever happens, Christopher is my son and I can't forsee he'll have any problems leaving school with the 3 'A's necessary to secure a place at one of the better universities.

3 GRADE A 'A' LEVEL PASSES?

No, a triple 'A' credit rating when he applies for his student loan.

year he may require you to drive his vehicle to Edinburgh and back as a precaution in case Compliance checks his milometer.

Club membership   Fine, as long as it's not one that your interviewer is still on the 18-year waiting list for. Ten years ago membership of the University Conservative Club was good and Labour Club bad; now it's the other way round. It's really quite hard to keep up.

Coloured paper   People who print their cv on coloured paper to draw attention to it are rather like people who wear coloured bow ties with a dinner jacket. Individuals, certainly, but would you really want to share an office with one?

Alex PEATTIE + TAYLOR

I NEVER CEASE TO BE AMAZED BY THE DETAILS PEOPLE PUT ON THEIR C.V.s WHEN APPLYING FOR JOBS, ALEX...

THIS APPLICANT FOR A SECRETARIAL POST INFORMS US THAT SHE'S PASSED HER GRADE 8 VIOLIN AND IS A MEMBER OF HER LOCAL CHAMBER ORCHESTRA.

IT'S RIDICULOUS. I CAN'T THINK OF A SINGLE POSITION WHERE THE ABILITY TO PLAY THE VIOLIN WOULD BE OF ANY USE WHATSOEVER CAN YOU?

HANG ON, CLIVE. I'M MAKING A PHONE CALL.

...YOU WERE SAYING?

Alex PEATTIE + TAYLOR

I'VE GOT A TABLE BOOKED FOR 12.45, NIGEL.

OH...EXCUSE ME ONE MINUTE, ALEX.

CHRISTINE! YOU'VE BEEN OPENING THESE LETTERS ADDRESSED TO ME. CAN'T YOU READ? THESE ENVELOPES ARE ALL MARKED 'PERSONAL'.

OH... YES..

SYMPTOMATIC OF THE DECLINING STANDARDS OF THE TIMES WE LIVE IN, ALEX. ONE'S GOT TO BE SO CAREFUL WHEN ONE'S HIRING PEOPLE THESE DAYS...

I'M SORRY.

YOU KNOW YOU'RE NOT SUPPOSED TO OPEN THESE LETTERS. I'VE TOLD YOU A DOZEN TIMES WHERE TO PUT THEM...

I KNOW...

STRAIGHT IN THE BIN.

EXACTLY. WE DO NOT ACCEPT JOB APPLICATION LETTERS FROM PEOPLE WHO CAN'T EVEN SPELL THE NAME OF THE DEPARTMENT.

PERSONNEL DEPARTMENT

Electronic delivery of a cv is perfectly acceptable provided you first delete the recipient list from the e-mail which will show your prospective employer how many of his competitors you are sending exactly the same personalised letter to.

Referring prospective employers to your personal Internet home page where more biographical details of yourself (i.e. photographs of your cat, sound clips from your favourite *Star Trek* episodes) can be found is at worst harmless. The possibility that an interviewer might combine both the intellectual curiosity to know more about a candidate plus the computer literacy to access the website are statistically so unlikely as to be negligible.

3 Name, Rank and Serial Number

Preparing for Your Job Interview

Your cv is now complete and ready to be mailed off to potential employers. Bear in mind that at peak times large organisations will receive over a hundred cvs per day, so some sort of selection method is inevitable.

Often this task will be farmed out to a response centre. Rest assured that this is unlikely to use any filtration process more sophisticated than the tried and tested method of binning all cvs that don't mention one of the universities that make up the British prototype Ivy League (i.e. Oxford, Cambridge, Bristol, Exeter and Durham).

Alex PEATTIE + TAYLOR

WE SHOULD NEVER HAVE ALLOWED HAWKINS TO SIFT THROUGH GRADUATES' C.V.s AND SELECT THE ONES TO BE INTERVIEWED.

HE'S JUST REJECTED ANYONE WHO DIDN'T GO TO WHAT HE PERCEIVES AS A "PROPER" UNIVERSITY.

IN THE PROGRESSIVE TIMES WE LIVE, WITH ALL THE SOCIAL CHANGES BEING EFFECTED TO BRING ABOUT THE CLASSLESS SOCIETY IT'S SAD TO SEE A RESPECTED COLLEAGUE EXHIBIT SUCH BLINKERED IGNORANCE.

I'M ASHAMED OF HIM...

I MEAN THIS CANDIDATE HAS BLATANTLY BEEN SELECTED JUST BECAUSE THE WORDS "OXFORD UNIVERSITY" APPEAR ON HIS C.V. UNDER "HIGHER EDUCATION"

HAWKINS REALLY IS AN AWFUL SNOB...

A TERRIBLE SNOB, CLIVE.

NOW, ANY SELF-RESPECTING HALFWAY-COMPETENT SNOB WOULD KNOW THAT 'OXFORD BROOKES UNIVERSITY' IS MERELY THE FLASH NEW NAME FOR OXFORD POLYTECHNIC.

RIP RIP   RIP

Alex PEATTIE + TAYLOR

WHAT DID YOU THINK OF THAT LAST CANDIDATE, CLIVE?

HARD TO KNOW REALLY...

WHAT CAN YOU SAY WHEN SOMEONE SPENDS THE WHOLE INTERVIEW GOING ON ABOUT HOW HE'S BOUND TO BE ON THE BOARD OF DIRECTORS WITHIN A FEW YEARS..

AND HOW HE'LL BE EARNING A MILLION A YEAR BY THE TIME HE'S 35 AND DESCRIBING THE YACHT AND HELICOPTER HE'LL OWN..?

WELL, HE WAS A GOOD LISTENER...

PERHAPS THERE'LL BE A PLACE FOR HIM IN COMPLIANCE.

I MUST SAY, ALEX, IT WOULD BE HELPFUL IF YOU'D LET THE NEXT ONE GET A WORD IN EDGEWAYS...

45

If left in the hands of the bank's staff, some less scientific selection methods may be practised. One story tells of a bored executive who threw a pile of cvs down a staircase and decided to interview only candidates whose résumés got to the bottom. Following a similar line of thinking, one apocryphal boss, when faced with a depressingly large stack of job applications on his desk, divided it into two halves and tossed one half in the wastepaper basket, saying that he wouldn't want to employ anyone who wasn't lucky.

If your cooked-up cv can get you through this rigorous selection procedure you will be called in for interview.

In the old days an interview for a bank consisted of a short chat about housemasters at the school you and your interviewer attended, followed by a pleasant lunch. As long as you knew how to patronise the wine waiter and in which direction to pass the port, the job was yours. One legendary story relates to an interview where the candidate was successful mainly because he was the only person sober enough to settle the bill after lunch.

Back then, apparently the standard application form for merchant banks included a section where you were asked to list any of your relatives who worked in the City. Though it's still worth slipping it in if your father is chairman of a FTSE 100 company, nepotism is now a little less institutionalised.

Alex PEATTIE + TAYLOR

I THOUGHT HOBBS PERFORMED RATHER WELL AT SECOND INTERVIEW. UNLIKE MANY GRADUATES HE SEEMED AWARE OF THE VALUE OF OLD-FASHIONED QUALIFICATIONS.

IN THESE TIMES OF POST-CRASH AUSTERITY ONE NEEDS TO IMPRESS ONE'S FUTURE EMPLOYER WITH SOMETHING MORE THAN A PAIR OF RED BRACES AND A BULLISH MANNER, AND HOBBS SHOWED A GENUINE UNDERSTANDING OF THE WAY THE CITY WORKS.

OK, SO HE PROVED HE COULD RECITE FACTS AND FIGURES PARROT-FASHION... BUT SURELY WE'RE LOOKING FOR SOMEONE WITH INITIATIVE, ALEX.

I THINK IT SHOWS GREAT INITIATIVE TO HAVE MEMORISED THE NAMES OF ALL THE MASTERS AT MY OLD SCHOOL.

IF HE HADN'T SLIPPED UP BY THINKING THAT "STIFFY" PILKINGTON TAUGHT GEOGRAPHY, I'D HAVE BEEN CONVINCED HE WENT THERE.

Alex PEATTIE + TAYLOR

YOU REMEMBER THAT RATHER PUSHY AND OBNOXIOUS YOUNG MAN WHO APPLIED FOR A JOB WITH US LAST MONTH?

PARKER? YES.

WELL, WE PUT HIM THROUGH QUITE RIGOROUS PERSONALITY PROFILING ANALYSIS TESTS AND HIS CONSISTENT RESULTS PROVE HIM TO BE CARING, OBLIGING AND SYMPATHETIC...

MY WORD.

WE'RE OBVIOUSLY GOING TO HAVE TO GIVE HIM A JOB - HE'S JUST THE SORT OF CHAP WE CAN USE.

... BECAUSE THE TESTS ARE SUPPOSED TO BE INFALLIBLE?

YES... AND SOMEHOW HE'S MANAGED TO FIDDLE THEM.

REMARKABLE.

47

Job interviews these days are rather more stringent and may involve several days of psychometric and graphology tests along with team-building and role-playing exercises. This reflects modern large organisations' more sophisticated approach to bottom-covering. If the person hired proves to be useless, rather than have to shoulder the blame themselves, the HR department can just sack the psychometric testing company.

PREPARING FOR YOUR JOB INTERVIEW

When arranging your job interviews, first be sure to schedule three or four for the same day. That way you can claim your train fare to London and back from each of the firms concerned and at least make a decent profit on the day even if you don't get any of the jobs.

Dress code City banks are foreign-owned nowadays, but it is still likely that you will be interviewed by a Brit. Thus, out of deference to the sensibilities of yesteryear, black shoes *with* laces are *de rigueur*. Your suit must be dark in colour and made of natural fibres, please, and nothing about you may be brown (apart from your nose). For women, a navy-blue suit is safe, with a cream blouse, discreet jewellery and knee-length skirt. Hemlines may fluctuate in the fashion world, but in the City they are fixed, like the Gold Standard (long = frump, short = secretary).

49

If you are applying to an American bank, then a white shirt with button-down collar and penny loafers is the prescribed uniform. Continental banks are a sartorial wasteland. Your interviewer may well be wearing a green or even check jacket so can hardly expect any better from you.

Facial hair Beards are still widely shunned and mistrusted in the City. A small goatee is an acceptable aberration in an IT engineer or Quant but will not be tolerated in other fields. During the time that Virgin was a public company, Richard Branson always felt that it was undervalued by the City. Ultimately, he found himself faced with two options: either to shave off his beard or to buy back his company. He chose the latter.

Of course, you will have done meticulous preparation. Bear in mind, though, that your interviewer will just have seen fifteen other candidates, all of whom have done identical preparation, namely

Reading that day's *FT* Though everyone does it on the train coming up to an interview, this is actually totally pointless. Your interviewer knows you will be up to speed on what happened in the City yesterday and will catch you out simply by asking you about an event lying in that region outside your financial expertise (i.e. anywhere from the day before yesterday back to the Devonian Age).

A much better idea is to go on the offensive. If you are passing through an airport, pick up the latest American business book (not yet published in this country) which will be full of buzzwords and hip management theory. Memorise a few of the more meaningless terms (Straight Through Processing, Heads Up, NOPAT Adjustment) and drop them into your interview. Your interviewer, who reads only John Grisham on flights, will be totally flummoxed.

Examples of skills You will have learned by heart an example from your life when you have shown each of the requisite qualities of:

(a)   leadership,

(b)   teamwork

(c)   communication skills

because you know they're going to ask you, and they know you know. So as you launch into the story of how you saved the passengers and crew of a 747 after you crashed in the Patagonian rainforest, your interviewer will interrupt you and ask for another example. So prepare two and start with the worst one.

Maths There will, of course, be a question to probe your powers of mathematical reasoning. A candidate in a job interview recently was asked: 'How many golf balls are in

the air in the UK at this moment?' A question like this will give your interviewer an idea of your mental processing ability and will give you an idea of where your interviewer would rather be right now.

Remember, your future boss needs to be assured that your basic numeracy is reliable. If you are to become his graduate trainee, he will be entrusting you with vitally important mathematical tasks where there is no margin for error, such as checking his lottery numbers on a Monday morning for him.

The one question you will always get asked and for which you must prepare a suitable answer is: 'Why do you want to work in the City?' This is actually a redundant enquiry in that both you and your interviewer already know the answer to it: viz. because you want to earn obscene amounts of money and retire to the Cayman Islands when you're thirty-five. The strange thing is no candidate ever says this at interview. Your interviewer didn't fifteen years before and you certainly aren't going to now. Instead you will mouth some laughable rubbish along the lines of: 'because it is a meritocracy where one can earn responsibility at an early age and express one's creativity in a structured environment.' Your interviewer will wince gently with remembered empathy.

These days all investment banks are global, integrated units into which American and

Alex PEATTIE + TAYLOR

I'M SORRY, ALEX BUT THIS CANNOT BE ALLOWED TO CONTINUE.

PARDON?

YOU'VE BEEN RUDE, AGGRESSIVE AND SARCASTIC TO THE LAST SIX CANDIDATES WE'VE INTERVIEWED. I'M OBLIGED TO SAY I THINK IT'S MOST UNFAIR.

CLIVE, THIS IS RIDICULOUS.

JUST BECAUSE YOU CONSIDER YOURSELF AT AN ADVANTAGE THAT'S NO REASON FOR YOU TO ALWAYS BEHAVE IN AN INTIMIDATING AND DOMINEERING FASHION DURING INTERVIEWS. IT'S TIME YOU TRIED SHOWING SOME CONSIDERATION AND RESTRAINT.

YOU'VE PUT THAT VERY FAIRLY, CLIVE.

...WHICH SHOWS YOU'RE ABSOLUTELY PERFECT AS MISTER NICE.

ALEX, I ABSOLUTELY INSIST THAT I BE ALLOWED TO BE MISTER NASTY THIS TIME.

NEXT!

THUMP THUMP

Alex PEATTIE + TAYLOR

RIGHT, NOW I WANT YOU TO IMAGINE THAT YOU'RE A SUCCESSFUL CORPORATE FINANCE EXECUTIVE COMING HOME AFTER A GRUELLING 12-HOUR DAY AT THE BANK...

YOU'VE GOT A STACK OF PAPERWORK TO GO THROUGH AND A BREAKFAST MEETING AT 7:30 THE NEXT MORNING. NOW, WOULD YOU GIVE UP YOUR SEAT ON THE BUS FOR AN OLD LADY?

ER.... YES... I MEAN, NO... ER... THAT IS TO SAY, YES.... I SUPPOSE SO...

RIGHT. THANK YOU. THAT WILL BE ALL...WE'LL BE IN TOUCH.

THANK YOU.

CLUNK

TCH TCH... TAKING THE BUS! OH DEAR...

RIP

RIP

55

Continental business techniques will have been assimilated. In the old days the foreign influence was felt only in the way that interviewers had clearly been watching too many war films and modelled their interviewing technique on Gestapo officers being played by hammy Brits.

Back then they might ask the candidate to open a window and see how many embarrassed flustered minutes you will spend heaving at it before you realise that the windows in an air-conditioned office are sealed. They would make you sit with the sun in your eyes (the closest they could get to actually shining a lamp in them). Or you would come into the interview room to find there was no chair. Or the interviewer would just sit reading a paper and totally ignore you.

All these late-lamented techniques were designed not to make you crack and blub out the details of Operation Mongoose but to find out how you handled the pressure, to see whether you would be able to take charge of a situation when you were expected to be subordinate.

Strangely enough, the City is one of those few worlds where training for such scenarios is appropriate. If you succeed in becoming a junior analyst or corporate financier or management consultant, you will spend much of your time telling people two or three

times older than yourself how to run their businesses. Dismissive contempt is definitely something you will have to learn to deal with.

Remember that your interviewer is choosing a person he or she will have to sit next to for ten hours a day for the indefinite future. On a per diem basis that's longer than they will spend with their spouse. And even though City job tenure is a short-lived thing nowadays, many of their marriages don't even make it that far. Evidence of a personality in a candidate is therefore important, unless you are applying to be a rocket scientist, in which case it is surplus to requirements.

The type of personality you display should, of course, be tempered by what field you want to work in. If it is Corporate Finance, talking too much in your interview will be perceived as a sign that you are indiscreet and not to be trusted with confidential information about your clients. In other roles – Stockbroking, for example – garrulousness is more desirable. After all, if you can't sell your cv to your interviewer, how on earth are you going to sell all those dodgy stocks to your clients?

Some days later you may receive a heartfelt rejection letter (with that upbeat first paragraph followed by the giveaway word 'unfortunately' heading up the second), which will be as expertly personalised as the application letter you sent to that and forty-six other banks.

Alex — PEATTIE + TAYLOR

YOUR SANDWICHES, ALEX...

HMM... I FEEL I MAY HAVE BEEN WASTING THE TALENTS OF A GRADUATE SUCH AS YOURSELF, BARNES. YOUR CHARACTER PROFILE SAYS YOU'RE SHREWD, TOUGH, ASSERTIVE, AMBITIOUS AND DEDICATED...

...IN SHORT ALL THE QUALITIES I PRIDE MYSELF ON POSSESSING... ADMITTEDLY THESE FINDINGS ARE BASED ON GRAPHOLOGICAL ANALYSIS, WHICH PERSONALLY I HOLD TO BE BUNKUM...

OH..

HOWEVER I'M PERSUADED THAT THERE IS A STRICT AND SCIENTIFIC CORRELATION BETWEEN HANDWRITING AND CHARACTER TRAITS, SO I'M PREPARED TO BELIEVE YOU MUST HAVE CERTAIN BASIC ABILITIES...

SUCH AS BEING ABLE TO FAKE MY SIGNATURE... SO GET ON WITH IT. THERE ARE 300 CHRISTMAS CARDS TO BE DONE.

Alex — PEATTIE + TAYLOR

ONE DAY I SUPPOSE ALL JOB INTERVIEWS WILL BE DONE BY CANDIDATES GOING INTO THEIR LOCAL VIDEO-CONFERENCING BOOTH AND TALKING TO US BY VIDEO LINK.

OH I DON'T THINK SO.

email: alex-cartoon@etgate.co.uk

CALL ME OLD-FASHIONED BUT I'VE GOT A STUDENT COMING UP FROM CAMBRIDGE FOR AN INTERVIEW TODAY AND I WOULDN'T DREAM OF INTERVIEWING HIM BY VIDEOLINK...

I STILL BELIEVE THAT THE EFFECTIVE WAY FOR A PROSPECTIVE GRADUATE TRAINEE IN HIS CIRCUMSTANCES TO GIVE A PROPER IMPRESSION OF WHAT CALIBRE OF CHAP HE IS, IS BY COMING TO THE BANK IN PERSON...

IE:- CONSPICUOUSLY STANDING ON CAMBRIDGE RAILWAY STATION WEARING A SUIT, OBVIOUSLY OFF TO A JOB INTERVIEW, IN FULL VIEW OF HIS FELLOW STUDENTS AND TWO MONTHS AFTER EVERYONE ELSE GOT THEIR MILK-ROUND JOBS... HA HA... WHAT A LOSER!

YOU REALLY ARE A SADIST, ALEX.

Failing this, you will receive a job offer. In keeping with the modern cut-throat world of graduate recruitment this may well be an 'exploding offer', i.e. one which automatically lapses if not taken up within a given frame of time, normally a week. This is to prevent you waiting for offers to come in from other banks and then choosing the most lucrative.

This well-intentioned attempt by your future employer to keep you untainted by the vices of treachery, duplicity and naked self-interest is about as likely to bear fruit as it is for a teenage offender, being sent for his first spell in prison and hanging around with a load of villains for three years, to come out and go straight.

4 Team Xerox

Being a Graduate Trainee in the City

With the applause of your double congratulatory First from Cambridge still ringing in your ears you arrive for your first day at work in your freshly pressed polyester suit only to find yourself handed a seventy-page offer document, pointed in the direction of the photocopier and told to run off forty-five copies by lunchtime. Blinking back tears of self-pity, you wonder what vicious crimes committed in a previous life have led you to suffer such indignity. Actually, this state of affairs comes about only partly out of the sadism and outdated belief in the fagging system shared by many of your superiors. The irony is that after years of having been the most brilliant student at school and college, you are now in the wretched position of being a person who doesn't know how to do anything.

The Catch-22 for the new bug is that the only way to learn traditional City skills like Stockbroking or Corporate Finance is by actually doing them. But, sadly, no Broker or Corporate Financier wants to have a clueless twenty-two-year-old attached to their desk.

On a trading floor, for example, the time it takes to explain to your junior details of the deal you are trying to pull off is also the time it takes for one of your rivals to stiff you on it.

The traditional solution to this problem was to give the graduate a report to write. This document was of no interest to anyone in the office; it merely kept the useless person out of everyone's hair, the idea being that by the time the report was completed the graduate would be due to be rotated to another department and the unwanted thesis could be quietly binned. Alex, not famed for his sensitivity to subordinates, has been known to request graduates to save him time by shredding their own reports.

The report ploy has been rendered less effective of late because the modern generation

of graduates is fully conversant with information technology and is able to download huge wodges of text, spreadsheets, graphs, etc. off websites or CD-ROMs in a matter of minutes and present it as their own work. This subterfuge cannot be detected unless someone actually reads the report, which, of course, would defeat the point of the original exercise.

The sad truth is that, despite being highly qualified and technologically literate, graduates are still good only for the following tasks:

(a)   doing photocopying;

(b)   getting sandwiches for their team;

(c)   showing their bosses how to download porn from the Internet;

(d)   having humiliating practical jokes played on them.

Points (a) to (c) are fairly self-explanatory. Point (d) involves some cautionary tales.

The classic gag played on a graduate in a financial environment is for you to be requested to find out a share price for the Venetian Tarmac Co., Royal Saudi Breweries or some other patently non-existent company. This is a bit like the gullible apprentice on a building site being sent to the stores for a tin of tartan paint. Everyone else is in on the joke and huge humiliation ensues unless the victim twigs quickly.

Alex
PEATTIE + TAYLOR

ONE IS ALWAYS TEMPTED TO ASSIGN THE NEW GRADUATES TO THE PETTY CHORES LIKE MAKING COFFEE, FETCHING SANDWICHES, AND TIDYING OUR DESKS...

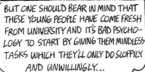

BUT ONE SHOULD BEAR IN MIND THAT THESE YOUNG PEOPLE HAVE COME FRESH FROM UNIVERSITY AND IT'S BAD PSYCHOLOGY TO START BY GIVING THEM MINDLESS TASKS WHICH THEY'LL ONLY DO SLOPPILY AND UNWILLINGLY...

I AGREE TOTALLY.

ONE REAPS THE BENEFITS FAR MORE IF ON THEIR FIRST DAY ONE SETS THEM SOME ACADEMICALLY CHALLENGING WORK LIKE WRITING A REPORT...

QUITE...

A WEEK LATER, WITH THE DEADLINE APPROACHING THEY'LL DO ANYTHING TO AVOID GETTING DOWN TO IT..

YOUR SANDWICHES, ALEX..

THANKS, ELLIS...ER... I THINK MY PENCIL NEEDS SHARPENING...

Alex
PEATTIE + TAYLOR

HONESTLY. I'M SO SICK OF HEARING SIMMS GO ON ABOUT THE AMOUNT OF WORK HE'S PUT INTO THIS REPORT HE'S WRITING FOR US...

YOUTHFUL EXUBERANCE IS FORGIVABLE IN A GRADUATE, CLIVE

HE'S TALKING ABOUT IT AS IF IT WERE HIS THESIS... IT'S ONLY SOME CRUMMY PROJECT WE'VE GIVEN HIM TO DO TO GET HIM OUT OF OUR HAIR IN HIS FIRST WEEK AT THE BANK.

NO-ONE GIVES A DAMN ABOUT HIM OR HIS REPORT. NO-ONE'S EVEN GOING TO BOTHER TO READ IT.

JUST TRY TO IGNORE HIM.

...HONESTLY, I'VE HARDLY OPENED A BOOK AND I HAVE TO HAND IT IN TOMORROW...

BESIDES, WE'VE ALL SEEN HIM SWOTTING IN THE LIBRARY....

At some point you will return from lunch to find a yellow sticky on your screen with the name and number of a client you are to phone urgently. Puffed up with pride, you dial the number and ask to be put through to Mr C. Lyon. 'Very funny,' replies the switchboard operator at London Zoo before putting the phone down on you.

Most of the practical jokes are highly puerile in nature, usually involving bogus memos from the company doctor instructing the graduate to leave an essential urine sample on some senior person's desk. Another classic ruse is secretly to place a mobile phone in the hapless trainee's briefcase and then invite you into a meeting. Naturally enough, ten minutes into the meeting the mobile rings and you are mortified to discover the source.

67

Women, as ever, come off best. The female trainee will be bullied less because of the fear of sexual harassment. At the same time a woman boss has the extra indignity at her disposal of being able to send her hugely embarrassed male graduate out to buy her a box of Tampax, 'Extra-large and extra-absorbent, please'.

But beneath all the indignities inflicted on the younger generation there lies an element of fear.

In the past the City was a non-vocational career, like teaching. People with wishy-washy Arts degrees just drifted into it while waiting for something better to come along. But with the advent of globalised markets and huge salaries since the Big Bang in 1986, the

financial world now attracts a different breed of candidate. These days all interviewees are fearsomely qualified, with straight As at school, first-class degrees in Applied Mathematics and postgraduate MBAs. And in the few hours off from heading up a bond-trading desk in their long vacation they worked for an AIDS charity. All this is rather alarming for Alex's old-school-tie generation, who secretly would admit that if presented with their own cv, detailing some indifferent A-levels and a 2:2 in History, they wouldn't even give themselves an interview.

The other change which favours the younger generation is the increasing reliance on information technology within the City. Obviously, all senior people will divert large

Alex — PEATTIE + TAYLOR

WELL, AFTER A YEAR AT MEGABANK BEING A LOWLY GRADUATE TRAINEE THIS IS MY CHANCE TO GET OUT AND DO SOMETHING USEFUL AND PROVE MYSELF...

WHAT IS?

ITS THE TIME OF YEAR WHEN ALL THE BANKS GO AND GIVE THEIR OXBRIDGE CAREER PRESENTATIONS AND THEY TAKE THEIR RECENT RECRUITS LIKE ME ALONG TO GIVE TALKS TO THE UNDERGRADUATES THERE.

OH REALLY?

YES, YOU SEE WORD-OF-MOUTH PERSONAL CONTACT REALLY MAKES A DIFFERENCE THERE... THE IDEA IS THAT I'LL MEET A LOT OF PEOPLE WHO MIGHT HAVE KNOWN ME WHEN I WAS STILL A STUDENT AND I'LL BE ABLE TO TALK TO THEM PERSUASIVELY ABOUT EMPLOYMENT OPPORTUNITIES.

AH YES...THE STUDENTS WHO WERE IN THE YEARS BELOW YOU?

ER...NO...THE ONES IN MY YEAR WHO WENT TO OTHER BANKS...THIS IS MY CHANCE TO NETWORK MYSELF ANOTHER JOB AWAY FROM THESE B*ST*RDS...

NICHOLS...ANOTHER SANDWICH PLEASE?

SCHEDULE

NOW I WONDER WHEN MINERAL BANK'S PRESENTATION IS?

Alex — PEATTIE + TAYLOR

OF COURSE THE CITY BOOM CAN'T GO ON FOREVER. ONE'S ALWAYS LOOKING OUT FOR THE ECONOMIC INDICATORS OF AN IMPENDING DOWNTURN...

PRET A MANGER

email: alex-cartoon@eetgate.co.uk

FOR EXAMPLE, IT'D BE WORTH STUDYING THE IMPLICATIONS OF THE SEEMINGLY UNTENABLE PROLIFERATION IN THE SQUARE MILE OF SERVICE INDUSTRIES IN THE FORM OF ALL THESE UP-MARKET FAST FOOD OUTLETS...

MARKS & SPENCER

ESPECIALLY AS THE FINANCIAL SECTOR IS CLEARLY OVER EXPANDED AND OVERMANNED, WITH AN UNFOCUSED AND OVERPAID WORK FORCE, ONE NEEDS TO LOOK NO FURTHER THAN OUR OWN BANK...

YES INDEED.

THAT STROPPY GRADUATE TRAINEE OF OURS...SO YOU THINK WE SHOULD GET HIM TO WRITE A REPORT ON SANDWICH SHOPS?

THEN HE'D HAVE NO EXCUSE FOR NOT GETTING OUR BREAKFAST...

amounts of the departmental budget into equipping their own offices with the latest Pentium-whatever-powered computer but will probably have to rely on their trainee to help them locate the on/off switch. Come-uppance is on the way, though, in the form of the new American-inspired work ethic in the City, which involves a systematic purging of all executives who do not know how to do a spreadsheet.

Of course, there will come a time when you, the trainee, will be a valuable member of the department. This time is the slack week between Christmas and New Year which no one else wants to work and you will be left on your own. It might be just the chance you've been looking for to make an impression on the rest of the

73

department by getting that top score on Tetris.

In waiting for your hour to come, the secret in the meantime is not to despair on the way to Starbucks. Graduates sometimes believe that they are unique in having been assigned the role of corporate skivvy. All your friends from college, you assume, are indeed working on the megadeals that they discuss in loud voices when you all meet up in the wine bar after work. Actually, it is a fair bet that none of them has done anything more glamorous that day than picking up their superior's dry-cleaning and that the only financial transaction they have been involved in is feeding pound coins into the meter their boss's car is parked on.

Slowly your anomalous position as the possessor of a sophisticated Palm Pilot, who has no clients or meetings to program into it, will change. You might even be entrusted with the odd miserable cantankerous client who never does any business and no one else wants to talk to. And at some point you will finally pass the required FSA exams, enabling you to transact business on behalf of the bank and deal with clients direct. This will be a cause for celebration among your team, who will want to toast your health in the local wine bar. Obviously you will not be invited, as you are now qualified to do 'lunch duty' and officially can be left to man the phones.

75

5 'I've Worked Damned Hard...'

Getting Your Bonus

We shall presume now that you have emerged from your awkward squirming graduate pupa into a fully fledged corporate high-flier. Maybe you drew yourself to the attention of your betters by volunteering to get coffee for the entire trading floor and then ran a black market operation with the complimentary cappuccinos you obtained courtesy of your Costa Coffee 'frequent-flier' card. Or maybe you did the opposite and deliberately got everyone's breakfast order wrong so often that they despaired of you as departmental handmaiden and assigned you some more responsible role.

Alex PEATTIE + TAYLOR

I SUPPOSE MY CHRISTMAS BONUS WILL BE RELATIVELY SMALL BY PREVIOUS YEARS' STANDARDS.

BUT THE VOLATILITY OF THE STOCK MARKET WILL MAKE THE TASK OF INVESTING IT MORE CHALLENGING.

ON WHAT YOU KNOW ABOUT THE PROBABLE STATE OF THE MARKETS, ALEX, WOULD YOU ADVISE ME TO PUT IT INTO SHARES?

ON WHAT I KNOW ABOUT THE PROBABLE SIZE OF YOUR BONUS, CLIVE, I'D ADVISE YOU TO PUT IT IN THE CHRISTMAS PUDDING.

Alex PEATTIE + TAYLOR

REMEMBER THE WAY WE USED TO TALK ABOUT ALL THE MONEY WE EARNED IN LOUD VOICES IN RESTAURANTS?

OH GOD YES. CRINGE!

WE WERE LUCKY PEOPLE DIDN'T DRAW SOME PRETTY UNFAVOURABLE CONCLUSIONS ABOUT US BECAUSE OF OUR IGNORANCE OF CITY ETIQUETTE.

I NOW REALISE THAT A PERSON WHO IS PAID A LOT OF MONEY DOES NOT GO AROUND BRAGGING ABOUT HIS SALARY IN PUBLIC PLACES.

CERTAINLY NOT.

IT'S REFERRED TO AS AN 'EMOLUMENT' AFTER £100,000 P.A.

THANK GOD WE ALWAYS STATED THE ACTUAL AMOUNTS.

Or maybe you copied the example of the legendary graduate trainee of City lore. You are handed a fifty-pound note by your boss, told to go to get breakfast for the team and 'get something for yourself'. On returning, you distribute the croissants and return to your desk. 'What about my change?' your boss demands. 'You told me to get something for myself,' you reply insouciantly. 'I got myself this pullover.'

Whatever it may be, some display of individuality of spirit has allowed you to gain the corporate promotion to the realm of the living. Your immediate task now is to secure yourself a bonus.

For all the hysteria in the press (whipped up by desperately envious underpaid financial

journalists) about outrageous City salaries, most people's basic pay is not that huge. The discretionary annual bonus is the X factor that will, in a good year, send your take-home stratospheric. This makes sense when you consider the cyclical nature of markets. In a Bear market any bank would be scuttled by its own cost base if it was obliged to pay its staff what it paid them in the previous year's Bull market. Thus, in bad years (the end of the 1980s, the beginning of the 1990s and 1998) many organisations pay out zero bonuses, and employees have to struggle by on their basic.

City pay packets should, like unit trust adverts, be marked with the warning: Remember, your total remuneration can go down as well as up. Sadly, for all their (professed) expertise with their clients' money, City people are notoriously useless at managing their own. Buoyed by the almost uninterrupted Bull market of the last twenty years, they gear themselves up with huge mortgages, forget the nominal word 'discretionary' that is attached to their bonus payment and get wiped out when the market turns down.

Make no mistake: you will be exactly the same. So your first problem is how to ensure you are actually paid the bonus you have already blown on a new flat and a Porsche 911.

Your discreet enquiries among your colleagues about expected bonus levels will be

Alex PEATTIE + TAYLOR

I CAN'T BELIEVE YOU'RE REACTING LIKE THIS AFTER I'VE JUST TOLD YOU I'VE FOUND SOMEONE WHO MAKES ME FEEL HAPPY AND I'M LEAVING YOU FOR HIM...

LOOK, DARLING...

...ALL I'M SAYING IS IT'S THE FIRM'S XMAS PARTY TONIGHT AND WE'RE BOTH EXPECTED...

TYPICAL! I TELL YOU I'VE BEEN HAVING AN AFFAIR AND ALL YOU CARE ABOUT IS YOUR WORK LIFE AND HOW THAT'S GOING TO BE AFFECTED...

OKAY, OKAY... I'LL COME WITH YOU AND FAKE IT FOR ONE MORE NIGHT... I'LL GO ALONG AND BE A HYPOCRITE AND PRETEND EVERYTHING'S THE SAME AS IT EVER WAS AND BE A SOCIAL ASSET...

THANK YOU, DARLING...

...JUST YOUR USUAL WHINGE TO MY BOSS ABOUT ME WORKING LATE ALL THE TIME AND NEGLECTING YOU... I DON'T WANT HIM THINKING I'VE BEEN SKIVING OFF JUST COMING UP TO BONUS TIME.

SO LONG AS YOU REALISE I DON'T ACTUALLY CARE ANY MORE.

SURE.

Alex PEATTIE + TAYLOR

NOW, ALEX, ABOUT YOUR BONUS:- NORMALLY YOUR PERFORMANCE THIS YEAR WOULD ENTITLE YOU TO A PRETTY GENEROUS CHRISTMAS REMUNERATION...

HOWEVER I'VE BEEN KEEPING AN EYE ON YOU THE PAST FEW MONTHS AND I'VE NOTICED YOU'RE FREQUENTLY GETTING INTO THE OFFICE LATE, GOING OUT FOR UNNECESSARILY LONG LUNCHES, OFTEN SLIPPING OFF EARLY IN THE EVENING.

I'M SORRY TO SAY WE'VE HAD TO TAKE THIS CONDUCT INTO ACCOUNT AND HAVE ADJUSTED YOUR BONUS ACCORDINGLY...

AH. A SUPER COLOSSAL ONE. GOOD. SO YOU'D SUSSED IT THAT I'D BEEN OUT MEETING HEADHUNTERS...

YES, AND SETTING YOURSELF UP WITH ANOTHER JOB TO BLACKMAIL US AS USUAL.

completely fruitless. City people will blab freely about confidential inside information pertaining to their clients, but the one subject no one will ever talk about is how much they get paid. Many of them don't even tell their own marital partners (well, it makes it easier to skimp on your divorce settlement that way).

Remember, there are no such things as salary scales in the City. People are paid whatever they managed to scam their boss into giving them by telling huge fibs about how much they were on at their previous bank. The hideous fear that gnaws at every City person's heart is that all the other people on the desk are getting paid much more than you. A sure way to strike terror and to foment discord in your office is to accidentally-on-

Alex PEATTIE + TAYLOR

RUPERT STERLING DIRECTOR

WELL, MELISSA, IT LOOKS LIKE WITH THE GREATEST OF RELUCTANCE I'M GOING TO HAVE TO TAKE THIS MATTER TO RUPERT IN PERSON...

OH. GO ON THEN.

I MEAN IT'S A DISGRACE. I ASKED YOU TO TYPE MY C.V. THREE DAYS AGO... THREE WHOLE DAYS MARK YOU... AND ABSOLUTELY NOTHING HAS HAPPENED...

REALLY, THIS IS THE ONE BASIC FUNCTION THAT WE EXECUTIVES RELY ON YOU SECRETARIES TO PERFORM ABOUT THE OFFICE...

...NAMELY SPREADING GOSSIP. I WAS RELYING ON WORD GETTING BACK TO RUPERT. THAT I WAS LOOKING FOR ANOTHER JOB.

LOOK: NO-ONE I TOLD RECKONED RUPERT WOULD THINK YOU WERE WORTH A RISE ANYWAY...

Alex PEATTIE + TAYLOR

I'VE GOT TO TELL YOU I'M STARTING TO GET EXTREMELY WORRIED ABOUT ALEX'S BEHAVIOUR...

I'M AFRAID HE MIGHT BE ABOUT TO SERIOUSLY MAKE A FOOL OF HIMSELF OVER HIS RELATIONSHIP WITH OUR NEW FEMALE BOSS JANE...

...LOOK HOW HE'S BEEN WRITING HER NAME OBSESSIVELY OVER AND OVER AGAIN ON HIS BLOTTER...

YOU THINK HE MIGHT HAVE BECOME INFATUATED WITH HER?

NO, I'M WORRIED THAT HE MIGHT HAVE AGREED TO SIGN ALL HER XMAS CARDS FOR HER OUT OF SHEER BONUS-TIME CRAWLING...

83

purpose leave your cv in the departmental printer, having sneakily doubled the figure for your salary.

In order to enhance your bonus to the maximum degree, two simple principles have to be observed:

(a)   take credit for any deals that have been successful;

(b)   distance yourself from any deals that have been a disaster.

There is no point in starting too early in the year. Deals done in February will be long forgotten by the time bonuses are assigned at Christmas, though this confusion can work to your advantage when retrospectively exaggerating your role in a given project at many months' remove.

Still, no analyst worth his salt will bother to produce any hard-hitting research early in the year. At worst the recommendations will be proved wrong, and if they're not you will be expected to replicate them. No, November, just before Santa brings round the bonus cheques, is the time to hit the market with your big idea.

Alex PEATTIE + TAYLOR

WELL, GENTLEMEN, THE STOCKMARKET IS BOOMING AND OUR OWN BUSINESS REMAINS PROFITABLE...

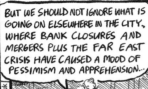

BUT WE SHOULD NOT IGNORE WHAT IS GOING ON ELSEWHERE IN THE CITY, WHERE BANK CLOSURES AND MERGERS PLUS THE FAR EAST CRISIS HAVE CAUSED A MOOD OF PESSIMISM AND APPREHENSION...

I ADVISE THEREFORE THAT WE EXERCISE FINANCIAL PRUDENCE AND REIN BACK ON ANY UNNECESSARY EXPENDITURE AT THIS TIME.

AGREED...

SO WE PAY OUT ZERO STAFF BONUSES ALL ROUND, ASSUMING THAT PEOPLE WILL BE TOO SCARED TO LEAVE...

RIGHT. WHICH MEANS WE CAN AFFORD THAT NEW GAINSBOROUGH AND THE QUEEN ANNE TABLE FOR THE BOARDROOM.

email: alex-cartoon@etgate.co.uk

Alex PEATTIE + TAYLOR

CAN I REMIND YOU THAT THE PURPOSE I'VE CALLED YOU INTO MY OFFICE IS ONE WHICH REQUIRES THE UTMOST SERIOUSNESS...

YOU ARE A VERY PROFESSIONAL P.A. AND I TRUST YOU WILL APPRECIATE THAT THIS IS NOT A MATTER FOR LEVITY...

NO, RUPERT, OF COURSE NOT...

DO I DETECT A <u>SMIRK</u> PLAYING ROUND THE CORNERS OF YOUR MOUTH, YOUNG LADY? GET RID OF IT...

I'M SORRY, RUPERT...

IT'S JUST THAT I GLIMPSED CLIVE BREAK INTO A COLD SWEAT OUT OF THE CORNER OF MY EYE.

TRY AND KEEP UP THE GRIM FACE. REMEMBER WE'RE TRYING TO LOOK LIKE WE'RE DISCUSSING DEPARTMENTAL BONUSES...

email: alex-cartoon@etgate.co.uk

85

Corporate financiers like to celebrate the successful signing of a deal by producing a 'tombstone' (a copy of the offer document embedded in Perspex). However, sometimes it may slip their minds to arrange for these to be made up until shortly before bonus season, when they will suddenly present their boss with a whole six months' worth of these commemorative artefacts in one go.

Of course, there is no need for you to have actually been involved in any given deal in order for you to take credit for it.

When a deal is started, it can be a good idea to volunteer for some minor role within it. Offer to do some photocopying or to help prepare a presentation. Your frankly

Alex PEATTIE+TAYLOR

I THINK IT'S NICE TO GET ONE OF THESE "TOMBSTONES" AFTER WE'VE WORKED ON A DEAL...

WELL, THEY'RE NORMALLY JUST A COPY OF THE COMPANY PROSPECTUS EMBEDDED IN PERSPEX. OPINIONS DIFFER ON THEIR VALUE...

FOR EXAMPLE ALEX IS WELL AWARE THAT THEY DON'T SERVE ANY OFFICIAL OR LEGAL FUNCTION BUT ARE JUST A MEMENTO FOR ALL RELEVANT PERSONNEL OF A DEAL ON WHICH ONE WORKED...

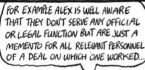

THAT'S WHY HE NEVER GETS ROUND TO HAVING ANY OF THEM MADE AT THE TIME AND ONLY BELATEDLY HAS THEM ALL DONE AGES AFTER THE EVENT...

JUST BEFORE THE BONUSES ARE TO BE PAID OUT?

QUITE. DELIVERING A WHOLE YEAR'S WORTH EN MASSE CRAFTILY DRAWS RUPERT'S ATTENTION TO HOW MUCH WORK HE'S DONE...

Alex PEATTIE+TAYLOR

THIS PRIVATE GYM THE BANK HAS INSTALLED HAS BEEN A MARVELLOUS INNOVATION FOR MANY PEOPLE...

email: alex-cartoon@etgate.co.uk

ESPECIALLY WHEN ONE CONSIDERS THAT MANY OF US SENIOR PEOPLE LIKE TO SPEND A LUNCHTIME SWEATING OFF THAT EXCESS FAT ON ONE OF THESE HI-TECH EXERCISE BIKES...

AMAZING ISN'T IT, HOW ONE IS PROVIDED WITH A CONSTANT INDICATION OF THE PRECISE QUANTITY OF WORK DONE AND THE EXACT TIME PUT IN...

YES INDEED...

THERE'S NO PEACE FOR A BOSS AT BONUS TIME...

I'VE REALLY SLOGGED MY GUTS OUT THIS YEAR... STAYED LATE EVERY NIGHT...

DO SHUT UP, CLIVE.

87

inconsequential contribution to the proceedings can be hugely inflated if the deal subsequently goes well, or discreetly forgotten if it bombs.

Once the deal is triumphantly concluded by people other than yourself, make sure you are the first to send round a global e-mail congratulating the relevant colleagues. If phrased succinctly, this may manage to suggest to outside parties (viz. those who are determining the bonuses) that you were in some way involved.

Or, go one better and organise the celebration drinks in the wine bar. Propose a toast to the successful team and relish the spectacle of them trying to drink champagne through gritted teeth.

Make lots of mentions in front of your boss of the crucial introductory meeting you had with the client in question (OK, it was only at a general presentation and there were fifty other people present, but you can gloss over this technicality).

Avoiding the fallout from deals that go belly-up is trickier. A good ploy is to ensure that at the beginning of any project you are involved in you send a warning memo to all concerned expressing your fears and reservations about the feasibility of the deal. All documentation relating to a deal is, of course, filed away and kept. Assuming the deal is a success, no one will ever have any need to look into the file. The only situation under

89

which it will ever be opened is if the deal proves to be a total dog and your boss is casting around for someone to pin the blame on. Only in this extreme situation will your arse-covering memo come to light and get you neatly off the hook.

In the run-up to bonus time itself (normally Christmas or early in the New Year, according to your company's year end) you need to engineer a few one-on-one interfaces with your boss to be sure that your personal contribution to departmental profitability is uppermost in his mind.

Air journeys are ideal for this. If you can sit next to your boss on even a short-haul flight you can mention how hard you've been working, even planting the suggestion subliminally in his brain as he snoozes next to you. It is for this very reason that many bosses travelling in business class insist their subordinates fly steerage.

Taxi journeys, even trips in the lift, though of shorter duration, can be pressed home to your advantage. If your boss is a smoker, you can make sure your nicotine cravings coincide with his and join him outside the building. Indeed, lifelong non-smokers have been known to take up the habit just before bonus time in order to buttonhole the master of their fate.

It will be a huge coup if you can manage to invite your boss over to your home for

Alex PEATTIE + TAYLOR

SO THIS 'LIFE COACH' YOU RETAIN GIVES YOU SORT OF THERAPY FOR YOUR CAREER? HOW OFTEN DO YOU SEE HER?

ACTUALLY, CLIVE, IT'S ALL DONE ON THE PHONE. I BOOK A MEETING ROOM ONCE A WEEK AND HAVE A CHAT WITH HER. FRANKLY I THINK IT'S A VERY PRUDENT AND FORWARD THINKING THING TO DO...

MORE THAN EVER AT THESE TIMES OF ECONOMIC UNCERTAINTY WITH LOOMING CUTBACKS IT'S ONLY SENSIBLE TO PURSUE ALL THE OPTIONS...

SO YOU USE THESE SESSIONS TO EXPLORE ALTERNATIVE PATHS TO SELF-FULFILMENT OUTSIDE THE WORK SITUATION..?

NO. I JUST HOPE RUPERT WILL ASSUME I'M TALKING TO A HEADHUNTER AND CONSEQUENTLY WON'T DARE DOWNGRADE MY BONUS...

email: alex-cartoon@etgate.co.uk!

Alex PEATTIE + TAYLOR

AS A LIFETIME NON-SMOKER, OBVIOUSLY I'M GLAD FOR HEALTH REASONS THAT THIS ORGANISATION HAS A SMOKING BAN.

OF COURSE

SO I GUESS YOU MUST HAVE STRONG VIEWS ON THE FACT THAT BY VIRTUE OF HIS POSITION OUR BOSS IS ABLE TO SMOKE IN HIS OFFICE...

I CERTAINLY DO.

AT MY LAST COMPANY THE SMOKING BAN WAS STRICTLY ENFORCED AND IF THE BOSS WANTED TO LIGHT UP HE HAD TO JOIN THE GAGGLE OF OTHER NICOTINE ADDICTS OUTSIDE THE BUILDING...

THAT MUST HAVE MADE A BIG DIFFERENCE PSYCHOLOGICALLY... YES...

...I WAS TOTALLY PARANOID...ESPECIALLY JUST BEFORE BONUS TIME, SEEING ALL THOSE BROWN-NOSING SMOKERS GETTING A CHANCE TO BUTTON-HOLE HIM IN PRIVATE... LONG MAY RUPERT CONTINUE TO FLOUT THE RULES, EH?

dinner at this crucial time. This will give you an unparalleled opportunity to impress on him how hard you've been working by pointedly falling asleep at the table.

If you cannot persuade him to come to dinner, book a table at his favourite restaurant and invite him to join you for lunch. If he refuses, simply use the table to entertain a well-known headhunter instead. Slipping the maître d' a generous tip should ensure that news of the person you were *tête-à-tête* with reaches the ears of your boss, who should automatically ratchet up your bonus a notch or two.

6 'Can You Talk...?'

Getting Yourself Headhunted

If all your efforts of the last chapter have come to naught your natural thought will be to find yourself a new employer who appreciates your talents. If, on the other hand, you were successful in negotiating yourself a handsome bonus you will no doubt feel you are now a person in demand and decide to sell your services elsewhere. Either course will involve being headhunted.

Naturally, you cannot approach a headhunter yourself. The only way to secure yourself a decent bump-up on your existing package is to suggest that you have no intention of moving jobs and are perfectly happy where you are. Thus, you will have to wait for a headhunter to call you.

Be warned, though: the first time you are called by a headhunter it will almost certainly be a wind-up by mischievous colleagues on your desk. They will derive huge amusement from observing your desperately defensive body language and your feeble attempts to cover up the surge of pride that goes through you as you hear those stirring words finally addressed to you: 'Can you talk?' Your 'headhunter' will then arrange a top-secret meeting at some local wine bar and ask you to turn up carrying some bizarre object as a means of identification. You will sneak off to the tryst at the appointed hour only to find that all your colleagues happen to be in the same wine bar and against their custom will insist on buying you drinks while you desperately try to get rid of them ahead of the anticipated arrival of your passport to a new job. At some point they will reveal the subterfuge and you will feel very foolish.

The first time you speak to a genuine headhunter you will probably not realise you are doing so as he will be posing as a market researcher or someone compiling a directory of City executives or a financial PR man arranging a golf day – anything to get a list of all

the people currently working in your department and their job titles. In your naïvety you will probably supply the required information. Don't forget to include your own name and raise your job title by a couple of ranks while downgrading those of all your colleagues.

You can, of course, reply to job ads in the paper. The problem here is that, apart from revealing that you are desperate and thus losing your salary-enhancing trump card, most recruitment adverts are for non-existent jobs. They are placed either by downmarket recruitment agencies looking for new candidates or by banks themselves wishing to find out how many of their own disloyal staff will apply for the post.

Similarly, be suspicious if you receive a call from a headhunter shortly before bonus time. He is probably in cahoots with your boss and conducting a loyalty survey. If you respond positively you will never hear from him again but will find your bonus downgraded to zero.

At some point, though, you will find yourself contacted by a bona fide headhunter who is genuinely interested in *you* (you will know this as he will describe the position he has been hired to fill and then ask you if you have a friend who might be interested; only a fool would supply any name other than his own). Your colleagues will, of course,

immediately twig what is going on from hearing one side of the conversation, which will go as follows:

YOU: Hello? . . . Speaking . . . (*suddenly sotto voce*) yes . . . er, no . . . Give me your number and I'll call you back.

If there is any lingering doubt in the minds of your colleagues, the fact that you then pick up your mobile phone and vanish into the corridor will seal it. All City banks are provided with several thousand hard telephone lines which employees may use gratis. Anyone who voluntarily courts brain cancer by using a mobile inside his place of employment is either talking to headhunters or dealing in insider information.

Sadly for you, although this person will be a recruitment consultant of sorts, he will probably be from some third-rate agency (after all, why else would he want *you*?). Desperate for some business to pay the rent on his run-down premises above a betting shop on Shoreditch High Street, he will simply mailmerge your cv to every bank in the City (most probably including, to your huge embarrassment, your current employer).

Alex — PEATTIE + TAYLOR

TELL ME, RICHARD, HOW DO YOU HEADHUNTERS GO ABOUT PREPARING A LIST OF THE JOB CANDIDATES WHO ARE TO BE CONSIDERED BY SOMEONE LIKE ME?

DO YOU JUST GET YOUR SECRETARY TO PULL OUT ALL THE RESUMÉS WITH "CORPORATE FINANCE" ON THEM?

GOODNESS ME, NO... IT'S VERY SCIENTIFIC...

I SEE. WELL THIS IS CERTAINLY A MOST INTERESTING SHORT-LIST. I'M MOST INDEBTED TO YOU. MIKE JAMES, FOR EXAMPLE... I HAD NO IDEA HE WAS ON THE MARKET...

AH... YOU KNOW HIM. VERY ABLE CHAP.

SADLY FOR HIM I BELIEVE I AM NOT ALONE AMONG EMPLOYERS IN THE CITY IN TENDING TO LOOK ASKANCE AT CANDIDATES WHO ARE CURRENTLY OUT OF WORK. I THINK MIKE'S GOING TO FIND IT HARD GETTING ANOTHER JOB.

ER... BUT SURELY HE'S *IN* EMPLOYMENT AT THE MOMENT...

TECHNICALLY, YES...

BUT I SHALL BE SACKING THE TREACHEROUS LITTLE WORM IN 10 MINUTES, RIGHT AFTER I'VE FINISHED SACKING YOU...

DRAT. HE WORKS HERE... DEBBIE BUNGLED AGAIN..

Alex — PEATTIE + TAYLOR

WHAT WERE YOU DOING ABOUT HALF AN HOUR AGO USING THE FAX MACHINE IN THAT SIDE OFFICE, CLIVE?

FAX MACHINE? SIDE OFFICE?

DON'T BOTHER TO DENY IT. I SAW YOU, AND WITH OUR BANK IN MERGER TALKS I THINK I CAN GUESS WHAT FURTIVE ACTIVITY YOU WERE ENGAGED IN.

WHAT ARE YOU SUGGESTING, ALEX?

ONLY THAT YOU MIGHT HAVE BEEN SNEAKILY FAXING DOCUMENTS IN RELATION TO A JOB OFFER AT ANOTHER BANK...

OH GOD... ALEX, I BEG YOU, PLEASE DON'T TELL RUPERT... IF HE FINDS OUT IT'LL BLOW EVERYTHING...

WHAT'S THIS ON OUR FAX MACHINE? A LETTER FROM ANOTHER BANK CONFIRMING A JOB INTERVIEW FOR CLIVE?

IGNORE THAT, RUPERT. HE FAXED IT TO HIMSELF TO MAKE HIMSELF LOOK WELL-BID...

email: alex-cartoon@eetgate.co.uk

99

Assuming that you have finally been contacted by a headhunter who has a genuine job on offer, you will now have to prepare for some interviews. This will involve updating your cv. Obviously, you will instinctively award yourself credit for every successful high-profile deal conducted by your current bank within the tenure of your employment there. The only other achievements you can validly list from your relatively short stay at the bank are training courses. Be wary, though, of including too many of these. Banks tend to send useless members of staff on lots of courses in the hope that being kept away from frontline work will cause the disgruntled employee to resign. You would not wish your cv to imply you were 'constructively dismissed' in this manner. It is also important to identify what

Alex PEATTIE + TAYLOR

I CAN SEE YOU ARE VERY INEXPERIENCED.. IN DEALING WITH CITY PEOPLE.. HAVE YOU NO UNDERSTANDING OR DISCRETION?

OBVIOUSLY I HAVE TO MAKE USE OF YOUR PROFESSIONAL SERVICES TO SECRETLY FIND MYSELF A NEW JOB. IN FUTURE PLEASE ALWAYS PHONE ME AT <u>HOME</u>...

IF YOU <u>MUST</u> CALL ME AT WORK AND ONE OF MY COLLEAGUES ANSWERS AND INFORMS YOU I'M OUT OF THE OFFICE, THEN JUST HANG UP OR SAY YOU'LL CALL BACK.

KINDLY DO <u>NOT</u> ANNOUNCE YOUR NAME AND THE COMPANY YOU WORK FOR AND DO NOT STATE THE EXACT REASON OF YOUR CALL TO ME...

I JUST SAID IT WAS YOUR DENTAL SURGERY CONFIRMING YOUR APPOINTMENT FOR NEXT WEEK.

BUT I'D TOLD EVERYONE I WAS AT THE DENTIST'S WHEN I WAS IN FACT OUT SEEING MY HEADHUNTER...

Alex PEATTIE + TAYLOR

WITH JOB CANDIDATES THERE IS MUCH TO CONSIDER BESIDES THE C.V.... LIKE BODY LANGUAGE...THE UNCONSCIOUS WAY A PERSON GIVES AN IMPRESSION OF HIMSELF IN A SOCIAL CONTEXT.

FOR EXAMPLE THERE'S THE TYPE OF PERSON WHO CREEPS DISCREETLY INTO A ROOM NOT MAKING EYE CONTACT WITH ANYONE, KEEPING CLOSE TO THE WALLS AND STAYING SOMEWHERE HE WON'T BE NOTICED.... THIS SAYS A LOT ABOUT HIM...

OF COURSE.

WHEREAS WHEN YOU MEET A CHAP LIKE HIGGS WHO NATURALLY STRIDES STRAIGHT TO THE CENTRE OF THE ROOM WHEN HE ENTERS AND TAKES POSITION THERE OF UTTER PROMINENCE AS IF BY RIGHT... WELL IT CREATES A POWERFUL IMPRESSION...

INDEED.

WHAT AN OAF! YOU SAY HE DID THAT IN CLARIDGES..? AT LUNCHTIME?

YES. WELL CLEARLY <u>HE'S</u> NOT HAD MUCH EXPERIENCE OF MEETING HEADHUNTERS.

CRUMPLE

the latest trendy format for cvs is and studiously ignore it. Anything too up to date will suggest that you have been coached by a professional and therefore that you were actually sacked by your last employer and are currently conducting your job negotiations from the cover of an outplacement agency.

Clearly you will need to concoct some sort of cover story to explain to colleagues your frequent absences from work when you are doing your job interviews. Classic ploys are to claim dental appointments, emergency meetings with clients, visits to sick relatives in hospital, and funerals of relatives. It will prove highly embarrassing if any of the aforementioned people phone you while you are supposedly visiting them (especially if it's the dead or seriously ill relative).

Of course, it is a hugely unfair world and, as ever, women have a colossal advantage over men when secretly interviewing for jobs. Unless her immediate superior is female, a woman can take as much time off work as she likes, claiming visits to the doctor. When her boss asks her what it is about she merely has to say 'feminine problems', knowing that he will be too hideously embarrassed to press her for any further details.

There are certain signs which will give away your covert interviewing activities to your colleagues, namely:

Alex PEATTIE + TAYLOR

OF COURSE IN THE DAYS BEFORE E-MAIL A COMPLEX INFRASTRUCTURE OF MESSENGERS AND SECRETARIES WAS REQUIRED TO PHYSICALLY DELIVER FILES, DOCUMENTS, MEMOS ETC BETWEEN DEPARTMENTS...

WHEREAS THESE DAYS ALL EMPLOYEES HAVE COMPUTERS WHICH ARE LINKED TOGETHER IN A HIGHLY SOPHISTICATED NETWORK, ENABLING THE INSTANTANEOUS ELECTRONIC TRANSFER OF DATA TO ANYWHERE IN THE BUILDING...

A TECHNOLOGICAL INNOVATION DESIGNED TO CUT DOWN ON THE NECESSITY FOR BANK PERSONNEL TO WASTE THEIR TIME SCURRYING AROUND FROM DEPARTMENT TO DEPARTMENT...

EXCEPT IN CLIVE'S CASE...

AH YES...

...SECRETLY PRINTING OUT HIS C.V. FOR A JOB APPLICATION AND IT HASN'T APPEARED ON ANY OF THE PRINTERS ON OUR FLOOR?

HE'D BETTER FIND WHICH ONE IT'S BEEN ROUTED THROUGH TO.... BEFORE SOMEONE ELSE DOES...

Alex PEATTIE + TAYLOR

YOUR HEADHUNTER ANY CLOSER TO LANDING YOU THAT JOB, CLIVE?

NOT YET, ALEX. IT SEEMS TO BE GOING ON FOR EVER...

AN ENDLESS ROUND OF MEETINGS AND INTERVIEWS AND LUNCHES WITHOUT ANY FINAL DECISIONS BEING MADE...THE CONSTANT ANXIETY OF TRYING TO KEEP IT ALL HUSH-HUSH... I TELL YOU, THE TENSION'S GETTING TO ME, ALEX...

I MEAN HOW AM I SUPPOSED TO CARRY ON WITH THIS MASQUERADE?

JUST REMEMBER TO KEEP A STIFF UPPER LIP, CLIVE.

OH YES... RIGHT.

...AND I SUPPOSE I OUGHT TO DRIBBLE WHEN I DRINK CUPS OF COFFEE TOO...

EXACTLY. FIVE "URGENT DENTAL TREATMENT" APPOINTMENTS IN ONE MONTH... IT'S ALREADY LOOKING SUSPICIOUS...

- you come into work looking unusually smart;

- you come into work wearing a suit on dress-down Friday;

- you are overheard talking to estate agents about acquiring an expensive new house;

- ditto upmarket car-dealers;

- when your graduate trainee comes round taking the morning sandwich order you decline (the clear implication being that you have already breakfasted with a headhunter);

- when discussion turns to the competitor you are about to defect to, you go quiet instead of slagging them off as usual along with everyone else in the office;

- you are observed photocopying your client records as booty to take to your new employer.

Hopefully, before you are rumbled you will have received an offer from another bank. You must now go in to see your boss and tender your resignation. One of three things will happen:

(a) your boss will beg you to stay and offer to match any salary you have been offered elsewhere. Though this seems to be the optimum outcome, it is actually rarely satisfactory and most people who have been bought back end up leaving the bank within a year. For a start, all your colleagues will hate you because you are now *definitely* being paid more than them. Your boss will hate you because you have

Alex PEATTIE + TAYLOR

BAD INTERVIEW, CLIVE?

I'LL SAY. I WAS LAUGHED OUT OF THE PLACE.

BLOODY HEADHUNTERS. ALL THEY CARE ABOUT IS THEIR COMMISSION. SO THEY ALWAYS SEND YOU FOR JOBS THEY KNOW YOU'VE HARDLY A CHANCE IN HELL OF GETTING.

WHY DIDN'T I STUDY THE DETAILS OF THE POSITION I WENT FOR MORE CAREFULLY? IT HAD A MUCH HIGHER LEVEL OF RESPONSIBILITY AND DYNAMISM THAN MY OLD JOB. I SHOULD HAVE TWIGGED...

IT WAS MY OLD JOB.

THE PEOPLE WHO WRITE THOSE ADS ARE TERRIBLE FIBBERS AREN'T THEY?

Alex PEATTIE + TAYLOR

WHAT? YOU MEAN HE'S BEEN SEEING YOU BEHIND MY BACK?

YES. HE ASKED ME OUT TO LUNCH 2 WEEKS AGO... I'VE BEEN SEEING QUITE A BIT OF HIM...

...BUT HE PROMISED ME HE WASN'T SEEING ANYONE ELSE... THE SMOOTH-TALKING CREEP... I SUPPOSE HE TOLD YOU ALL THE SAME LIES AS WELL...

I GUESS SO...

...LIKE HOW I WAS THE ONLY ONE... THE IDEAL HE'D SPENT AGES SEARCHING FOR... HOW I WAS REALLY SPECIAL...

YEAH, YEAH...

YOU'D THINK HE'D HAVE CONSIDERED HOW HUMILIATING THIS COULD BE FOR US... WHAT WE MIGHT FEEL IF WE EVER FOUND OUT ABOUT EACH OTHER.

YES...

HE MIGHT AT LEAST HAVE PUT US IN SEPARATE WAITING ROOMS SINCE WE'RE UP FOR THE SAME JOB.

BLOODY HEADHUNTERS. THEY'RE SO INSENSITIVE..

INTERVIEW ROOM

taken an unnecessary chunk out of his departmental budget which he could otherwise have paid to himself. Rest assured that your disloyalty will not be forgotten and the next time there's a cost-base rationalisation programme your name will head up the list of staff to be downsized, your grossly inflated salary representing an even bigger saving that it would previously have done;

(b)   your boss will accept your resignation and you will have the humiliation of being marched straight off the premises without even the chance to say goodbye to (i.e. boast to) your colleagues;

(c)   your boss will accept your resignation and, even more humiliatingly, make you work out your period of notice, thus demonstrating to all and sundry (and your new employer in particular) how unimportant you are.

It is normal for banks to debrief departing staff in an exit interview, though why they think that anyone who is off to work for a competitor would furnish them with any useful information about their company is a mystery.

Resist the temptation to tell your boss exactly what you think of him. You've been so preoccupied with your own clandestine job negotiations that you haven't noticed *his* frequent absences. He's been out interviewing, too, and could well end up as your Head of Department again a year or two down the line.

Panel 1: So you decided to keep Wilks on and have him serve out his notice after he resigned? — Yes, he's a competent banker after all.

Panel 2: Obviously the usual thing is to get an employee to leave immediately and take a couple of months off before starting work with his next employer... but we decided to take a pragmatic view...

Panel 3: It's a question of whether one lets someone use their time gainfully doing a proper job of work as a merchant banker or just idle away two months doing nothing getting bored and frustrated to the advantage of no-one.

Panel 4: i.e.:- Being kept back here at the office while everyone else in the financial community is out networking frantically at Ascot, Lords, Wimbledon, Henley... — Quite. At least this way he can't poach any of our clients...

Panel 5: Well, it's hardly surprising timing is it? After all, everyone's bonuses were paid out 3 days ago... — What?! Our boss has resigned?...

Panel 6: I imagine he waited for the cheque to clear, then went in to the chairman and told him he was off to another job... — He's run this department for five years... and now he's gone? Just like that?

Panel 7: I feel totally poleaxed... just numb and empty... I'm overwhelmed by a huge sense of loss and regret and despair... — I'm sorry, old chap. We all know what you thought of him... PAT PAT

Panel 8: ...that he was a total old S - H - ONE - T... — Exactly. And I was SO looking forward to telling him so to his face later this afternoon when I plan to hand in my resignation. DAMN... DAMN.

email: alex-cartoon@etgate.co.uk

111

7 The Tin Tack

Being Made Redundant

Everyone in the City gets sacked at some point in their career. There is no shame in it. In fact it is something of a badge of honour, like an RAF fighter pilot in the Second World War who could not consider himself blooded until he had been shot down a couple of times. After all, everyone knows Douglas Bader, but does anyone remember the names of the countless ace fliers who never got pranged?

One of the reasons why redundancy is considered merely an occupational hazard in the City is that the method of selecting those for the chop is fairly arbitrary. Following the American corporate model, modern financial institutions perfectly mirror the tendency of the world economy to alternately expand and contract. In the boom stage of the cycle

a bunch of useless people will be hired, and in the bust phase a load of perfectly competent people will be sacked. It's really nothing personal.

So, at some point in your tenure at your bank one of the following things will happen:

(a) there will be a downturn in the stock market;

(b) your bank will merge with another organisation;

(c) your bank will hire some management consultants.

Whatever the root cause, the result will be the same: the bank will implement a structured programme of cost-base rationalisation. Now a City firm has only one major overhead (i.e. the hugely overinflated salaries it pays its staff). Thus, there is only one realistic way to cut costs: by sacking people.

Of course, minor cost-cutting programmes can be implemented: forcing all employees to take all their business travel on no-frills airlines, for example, or reducing the per capita limit on client entertainment. But on a strict utilitarian basis it makes more sense to make a couple of people miserable by sacking them than to incite insurrection in a whole

department by depriving them of their complimentary in-flight champagne. And if your people can only afford to entertain at *Cats*, be assured your clients will find a competitor who can offer them the full monty at Glyndebourne.

Non-sacking alternatives to cost-cutting can also backfire badly. Back in the days before the omnipresence of e-mail, when banks used to employ armies of messengers to deliver documents to other banks, one organisation decided to save a few pennies by cancelling the free milk provided in the messengers' refreshment room. Naturally, the aggrieved couriers mentioned this fact to every single person they dropped a package off with. Hence, within a matter of a few hours all the bank's major rivals were aware that it was in financial trouble.

If you are unlucky enough to get sacked, console yourself that it is most likely your boss's incompetence that is to blame. The Board of Directors will have arbitrarily decreed that there must be a ten per cent head-count reduction across the board (by the way, this doesn't mean the board as in *the Board*; 'across the board' actually means everyone *except* the Board). Note that these cost-cutting targets are usually expressed in head-count reduction rather than in hard cash savings. If it was just a question of clawing back a few million quid, this could easily be achieved by firing a couple of senior directors.

Alex PEATTIE + TAYLOR

I MUST SAY I FEEL A LOT MORE COMFORTABLE ABOUT SACKING ATKINS THAN I WOULD HAVE DONE TWO YEARS AGO.

THE JOBMARKET OUT THERE HAS REALLY CHANGED SINCE THE BANKS WERE ALL CONTRACTING THEIR OPERATIONS WHEN THE ECONOMIC OUTLOOK WAS BLEAKEST.

AT THE MOMENT WITH THE BUSINESS CLIMATE HEALTHIER, THE STOCKMARKET AT AN ALL-TIME HIGH AND A MOOD OF REAL OPTIMISM ABOUT, IT'LL BE TOTALLY DIFFERENT FOR ATKINS WHEN HE GOES TO SEE HEADHUNTERS...

YES. THEY'RE BOUND TO REALISE THAT HE WAS USELESS AT HIS JOB.

QUITE. WHEREAS IN THE OLD DAYS HE COULD HAVE CLAIMED HE WAS JUST A VICTIM OF THE RECESSION.

Alex PEATTIE + TAYLOR

AFTER OUR DISASTROUS FINANCIAL YEAR, WILD RUMOURS ARE SWEEPING THE BANK ABOUT THE EXISTENCE OF A HIT-LIST OF 900 EMPLOYEES TO BE SACKED...

I'M AWARE OF THAT...

NOW YOU AND I KNOW THEM TO BE UNTRUE, BUT NEVERTHELESS THE BANK'S FINANCIAL PLIGHT IS A MATTER OF THE GRAVEST IMPORT...

I'M SORRY, DAVID, BUT AT TIMES OF CRISIS ONE CAN'T AFFORD TO NEGLECT THE NORMAL DAY-TO-DAY RUNNING OF ONE'S DEPARTMENT.

NOW IF YOU'LL EXCUSE ME, I NEED TO TALK TO A MEMBER OF MY TEAM ON A ROUTINE CLERICAL MATTER.

REALLY, RUPERT...

YOUR OBSESSION WITH PURSUING PETTY BUREAUCRATIC PROCEDURE AT A TIME LIKE THIS I CAN ONLY PUT DOWN TO ONE THING...

OH, CLIVE... COULD YOU POP IN AND SEE ME?

...SHEER WILFUL SADISM...

IT'S ONLY TO DISCUSS HIS EXPENSES, BUT HE'S NOT TO KNOW THAT...

UTTER TERROR

TREMBLE

117

This, sadly, is not how hierarchical organisations work. As the targets to be met are purely numerical, the people who get sacked will be those with the least power. These will by definition be the most junior and, of course, most lowly paid employees. Hence, any actual cost-saving will be minimal. The various Heads of Department will squabble over whose team should bear the brunt of the downsizing. So if it's you who ends up holding the brown redundancy envelope when the music stops, it is because your boss is a spineless wimp who was unable to stand up for his people.

For a City employee it is not possible to feel any real grievance if you are sacked, any more than an eight-year-old could validly complain if apprehended by a passing policeman some hours after having broken into a sweetshop. After all, the only reason you wanted to get into this world (regardless of what you told your interviewer) was for the megalithic salaries. But your remuneration to the tune of several hundred times the minimum wage is also a liability.

What should you do if you hear rumours that your department is about to be downsized? Clearly, you should set yourself up with a new job, but under conditions of utmost secrecy. If your employer gets wind that you have a bolt hole lined up, he will wait for you to resign rather than waste money by sacking you and having to pay you off.

Alex PEATTIE + TAYLOR

YOU HEAR SEBASTIAN'S BEEN DISMISSED BY THAT MAN-HUNGRY WOMAN BOSS OF HIS?

OH DEAR. WHAT HAPPENED?

IT'S A STORY THAT CAN ONLY HAPPEN NOWADAYS... ATTRACTIVE YOUNG MAN GOES OUT FOR THE EVENING WITH HIS SINGLE FEMALE SENIOR EXECUTIVE COLLEAGUE... HE AGREES TO GO BACK TO HER PLACE FOR A NIGHTCAP...

UNKNOWINGLY HE PUTS HIMSELF IN A VULNERABLE POSITION BECAUSE OF THE UNACCUSTOMED PHYSICAL INTIMACY... IT'S LATE, THEY'RE ALONE TOGETHER... SEXUAL SIGNALS BETWEEN THEM ARE MISREAD WITH THE CONSEQUENCE THAT ONE PERSON ENDS UP FEELING ANGRY AND REJECTED...

SO WHAT HAPPENED?

APPARENTLY HE SAID "WELL I DON'T KNOW ABOUT YOU BUT I THINK I'M ABOUT READY FOR THE SACK..."

TWIT. HE WAS ASKING FOR IT WASN'T HE?

Alex PEATTIE + TAYLOR

SWOTTING UP ON YOUR SACKING TECHNIQUE AGAIN, CLIVE?

DON'T MOCK, ALEX. I'VE GOT TO TELL CRISP TOMORROW THAT HIS JOB IS BEING AXED...

HOW TO SACK AN EMPLOYEE

IT FILLS ME WITH DREAD—THE THOUGHT OF HAVING TO DEAL WITH HIS SHOCKED REACTION—TEARFUL HYSTERIA OR NUMBED INCOMPREHENSION—WHEN I DELIVER THAT BOMBSHELL OUT OF THE BLUE...

HOW TO SACK AN EMPLOYEE

AND YOU THINK THAT READING THAT BOOK MIGHT HELP YOU TO SOFTEN THE BLOW?

HOW TO SACK AN EMPLOYEE

IF DONE OSTENTATIOUSLY ENOUGH, YES.

I SHOULD TRY LEAVING IT LYING AROUND ON YOUR DESK AS WELL... I DON'T THINK HE'S GOT THE MESSAGE YET...

HOW TO SACK AN EMPLOYEE

119

You should also take the precaution of swiping your corporate Amex card at various local wine bars to the tune of several hundred pounds. Thus, when the axe descends you will have huge amounts of credit in booze which can be used for leaving drinks, entertaining business contacts, wooing prospective new employers, etc., all at your ex-employer's expense.

As ever, women have a major advantage in this scenario. As soon as the first whisper of redundancies hits the grapevine, announce that you are pregnant. Your job is now totally safe. Your 'condition' will also give you a foolproof excuse for lots of visits to the doctor to cover up meetings with a headhunter. If the redundancy rumours should prove

121

groundless, just drop the pregnancy. No one (of the male sex, at any rate) is going to risk you bursting into tears by subsequently enquiring about it.

How will you know that you have been sacked? One of several scenarios will occur:

(a)   due to an unfortunate leak to a journalist, you will read about it in your morning newspaper on the way into work;

(b)   when you arrive at the bank, your entry swipe card will not work;

(c)   sitting at your desk, you will be unable to log on to your computer because your access code has been cancelled;

(d)   or, more unusually, you will be called in to see your boss with the head of Human Resources present and told the news.

Nowadays sacking is a much more humane activity, governed by the Helsinki Human Rights Convention, and all the heady exuberances of the 1980s are no more. One bank back then famously called its employees in over the tannoy one by one to the Human Remains department to be handed their P45s. In another instance employees arrived at

123

work to find black binliners had been thoughtfully left on their desks.

Such matters are handled more delicately in these enlightened and litigious times when sacked employees can sue their bank for harassment. Staff tend to be let go in dribs and drabs rather than shipped out en masse, and your redundancy notice may well be biked over to your home on a Saturday morning rather than handed to you in person in front of your colleagues.

In the same way that delivering the news has become more discreet, so has getting one's revenge on an ungrateful employer. In the 1980s a famous and probably apocryphal story tells of a dismissed trader who drove his company Porsche up to the bank's foyer, set off the car alarm, locked the doors and dropped the car keys down a nearby drain. Employees, on being given the bombshell, routinely smashed up their desks and phones.

These days a more subtle form of retribution is called for. Recently, a disgruntled downsized employee turned his bank's website into a hard-core porn page. Due to the computer illiteracy of his bosses it took them a good many hours to discover the switch. It is recorded that the bank got a record number of 'hits' that morning. Indeed, the hideous damage that IT staff are able to inflict on their employer's hardware has made

Alex PEATTIE + TAYLOR

HELLO. IT'S CLIVE PHONING DOWN FROM THE CORPORATE FINANCE DEPARTMENT ON THE TENTH FLOOR... SORRY TO BOTHER YOU AGAIN BUT IT'S MY COMPUTER...

YES... EXACTLY THE SAME THING HAPPENED AGAIN. I TRIED TO ACCESS A PROGRAMME BUT THE SYSTEM WOULDN'T LET ME LOG ON...

WHAT?... LOOK I'M SORRY BUT THIS IS YOUR DEPARTMENT'S BUSINESS... ALL I'M ASKING IS FOR YOU TO RUN A FEW SIMPLE CHECKS FOR ME... THANKYOU... YES, I'LL HOLD...

ALL RIGHT. THE ANSWER IS NO... YOU HAVE NOT BEEN SACKED AND YOUR ACCESS CODE HAS NOT BEEN CANCELLED.

PERSONNEL DEPT

PHEW... IN THAT CASE I'LL GET ON TO THE SERVICE ENGINEERS.

Alex PEATTIE + TAYLOR

SO YOU'RE SAYING YOU COULD SUPPLY THE BANK WITH PERSONALISED ITEMS EMBLAZONED WITH OUR COMPANY LOGO...

THAT'S RIGHT... AND IT'S NOT JUST AS CLIENT GIFTS EITHER...

EVERYONE KNOWS HOW IMPORTANT IMAGE AND VISIBILITY IS IN THE CITY... IF THE BANK CAN MAKE AVAILABLE A STYLISH GYM BAG OF ITS OWN FOR EMPLOYEES TO CARRY AROUND IT SHOULD MAKE GOOD BUSINESS SENSE...

HMM... I DON'T KNOW...

LOOK WHEN TIMES HAVE BEEN TOUGH SURELY THAT GIVES RISE TO THE OPPORTUNE MOMENT FOR STAFF TO BE PROVIDED WITH THINGS LIKE THIS IN ORDER TO BOOST THEIR MORALE...

WELL YES... YES, I CAN SEE THAT...

OKAY, SMYTHE:- YOU'RE REDUNDANT... NOW:- CAN I INTEREST YOU IN PURCHASING THIS NATTY SPORTS BAG TO LUG YOUR POSSESSIONS OUT INTO THE STREET IN... INSTEAD OF THAT EMBARRASSING TELL-TALE BLACK BIN LINER?

MEGABANK GYM BAG

125

them virtually unsackable. It is certainly the department of choice to be employed in during a recession.

If you are to be made redundant the scenario to aim for is know as Passing Go Three Times. This involves, in quick succession:

(a)   being paid your bonus;

(b)   being made redundant with a large payoff;

(c)   starting a new job with a big Golden Hello.

There may also be a couple of months of enforced 'gardening leave' between (b) and (c) when you are being paid to do nothing, which is the icing on the cake. Pulling off this brilliant coup will give you more satisfaction than any business deal you will ever conclude on behalf of your bank.

The marvellous thing about working in the City is the Bigger Mug principle. Your current employer may have seen through you, but in boom times (which, of course, if not actually happening are just around the corner) there is always some other organisation (usually some slightly spivvy German or Dutch bank desperate to break into the London market) who will not only give you a job but will also pay you more money.

At some point you will fall through the bottom of this distinctly rotten edifice, but by this stage you should have made enough money on various Golden Hellos and redundancy packages, trading alternately on your brilliance and uselessness, to retire and go and set up that cocktail shaker importing business you always dreamed of.

I NEED A WEE!

Sue Hendra & Paul Linnet

For our Alan, with love

I NEED A WEE!

SIMON AND
SCHUSTER

London • New York
Sydney • Toronto • New Delhi

Alan the bear loved whizzing down the helter-skelter with his friends.

WAHOOO! WHEEEEE!

It was SO MUCH FUN!

"Let's go on again!" said Alan.

"Alan, why are you dancing?"
asked Giraffe.

"I'm not dancing!" said Alan. "I need a wee!
But first I need just one more go."

"No," said Giraffe. "When you've got to go,
you've got to go."

But getting Alan to the toilets
wasn't going to be easy.

"Ooooh, just one balloon!"
he cried.

"Alan, come on, before it's too late,"
said Giraffe.

Then Alan saw Claude's party.

"Ooooh, just one piece of cake!" he cried.

"No time!" said Robot.

Finally they got there.

"Oh dear," said Giraffe. "Can you hold on?
It's going to be a long wait."

"But I can't wait," said Alan . . .

"I NEED A WEE!"

"Don't worry!" called a little dolly.
"I can help. You can come to my house!"

"PHEW!" said the friends.

"Oh no! I can't wee in there," said Alan.
"It's a teeny tiny toilet!"

And off he went.

"No! You can't wee in there!" whispered Robot.
"It's a teapot – not a wee-pot!"

"How about this hat?" said Alan. "It's perfect."

And he was just about to
have a wee when . . .

"Don't even think about it!"
said Magic Rabbit.

"Yikes! Sorry," said Alan,
dancing about again. "It's just . . ."

By now things were getting desperate.

"Quick, behind that curtain!" shouted Robot.

But when Alan turned around, he realised he was dancing furiously in front of a huge audience!

The crowd whooped. They cheered.
They'd never seen dancing like it!

"And the winner of the international toy dancing competition is . . ."

"Alan, my name's Alan."

"And how do you feel to have won
the cup, Alan?"

"Ahhhhh!" said Alan at last.
"I feel fantastic!"

"Well, what a relief," said Robot, smiling. "Thank goodness you don't need a wee any more."

"Oh no, I definitely do!" grinned Alan.

SIMON AND SCHUSTER
First published in Great Britain in 2015
by Simon and Schuster UK Ltd
1st Floor, 222 Gray's Inn Road, London, WC1X 8HB
A CBS Company

A CIP catalogue record for this book is available
from the British Library upon request

978-1-4711-2088-6 (HB)
978-1-4711-2087-9 (PB)
978-1-4711-2089-3 (eBook)

Printed in China
3 5 7 9 10 8 6 4

The End?

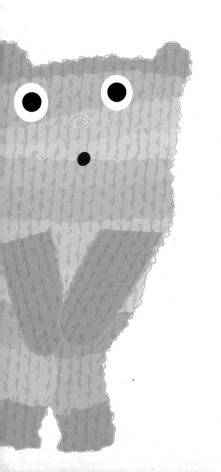